EASY STORIES IN ENGLISH FOR PRE-INTERMEDIATE LEARNERS

10 FAIRY TALES TO TAKE YOUR ENGLISH FROM OK TO GOOD AND FROM GOOD TO GREAT

ARIEL GOODBODY

Cover design by Geoffrey Bunting

Print ISBN 978-1-914968-01-3

Some of these stories were originally released at
EasyStoriesInEnglish.com

CONTENTS

WHY YOU MUST READ

'Why do I need to read in English?'

My students often ask me this. They think, 'I go to classes, I do my homework, I watch films in English. Why should I read books?'

They're wrong. In fact, reading is the best way to improve your English. Let me tell you why.

First, reading skills are more important than ever. That's true for English as well as your native language[1]. In 2006, only 1 in 100 people went to university. Now, 7 in 100 people go to university[2]. All jobs need more reading and writing than 100 years ago[3]. This is true for everyone, from office workers to mechanics.

Second, reading is the best way to improve *all* of your English. Reading will improve your speaking, writing, vocabulary and grammar better than any other method. It won't improve your listening skills, but it will improve your vocabulary. And when you have a better vocabulary, you can listen more easily, and improve your listening skills that way.

We're not talking about any kind of reading, though. In school, you probably read lots of English. Boring textbooks and stories with exercises at the end.

No, we're not talking about that. We're talking about reading for *pleasure*.

That means reading a book you enjoy because you enjoy it. Not because your teacher told you to read it. Not because it's what good students read. No questions, no exercises. Just reading for pleasure.

You're probably thinking, 'That's too good to be true.'

Let me show you.

In 1965, an experiment was carried out in juvenile delinquent reform centres[4] in America. One group of the students got free books. They were exciting books for young boys, such as *James Bond*. Normally, in experiments like this, they have lots of rules. Students have to read a book a week, and they have to do exercises. But in this experiment, they didn't have to do anything. They just gave them the books, and the boys could do what they wanted. They could throw the books away, give them back, or draw on the pages.

But the boys *did* read them. They read a lot of them. Some of them read a book every two days.

At the end of two years, they tested the students. Their reading and writing improved a lot, and so did their attitude towards school. But the students who did not do the experiment stayed the same. In fact, some of them got *worse* over the two years.

This isn't just for native speakers[5], either. A study[6] of English as a Second Language (ESL) students in the Fiji islands[7] looked at three methods: traditional English teaching, sustained silent reading[8], and a method where the teachers read aloud to the students[9].

By the end of the first year, the two reading methods were winning. Students who did those methods were 15 months ahead in their English ability. Students who did the traditional method were only 6.5 months ahead. They did the same experiment in Singapore, and found that the students who did sustained silent reading did the best in grammar tests. But they hadn't had any grammar classes! The students who did *only* grammar classes did worse than the students who only read!

When we do grammar exercises, we try to remember all the rules of the language. When we read, we *absorb*[10] them.

But I know what you're thinking: 'When I pick up a book in English, it's too hard for me! I get bored of looking up words, and I give up after a few minutes.'

That's why I wrote this book. Hopefully, it will make you fall in love with reading, by providing fun, familiar stories that are easy to understand.

The stories get harder and longer as they go, so you can feel like you're improving as you read. Most of the stories first came out on my podcast[11], *Easy Stories in English*, but I improved them for this book. Also, before there was only one level for each story, but now you can read all the stories at beginner, pre-intermediate, intermediate or advanced level. The stories are a mix of popular and less popular fairy tales[12], as well as one that I wrote myself.

Again, I know what you're thinking: 'Fairy tales? But those are for kids! I need *useful* vocabulary, about business and science and technology. There's no way to make that fun!'

Actually, there isn't such a big difference between Important Language and Fun Language[13]. We use a wide range of words when talking about technical[14] topics as well as chatting with our friends.

A study[15] by McQuillan[16] looked at vocabulary in 22 novels and found that they included 85% of words on academic word lists[17]. Rolls and Rogers[18] found that, if a student read a million words of science fiction, they would learn many of the technical words needed for a science degree.

So yes, reading fairy tales will help all of your English, even academic English. As an English teacher, I've seen many times that the students who do the best are those who read the most. For IELTS, for university, for business or just for travel, the students who read do the best.

But I understand if you still don't believe me. When I learned about all this, I found it hard to believe, too. But I like to try new things, and I love learning languages.

So in 2017, I decided to test these ideas[19]. I had wanted to learn Spanish for a long time, but I had tried traditional methods and not learned very much. I made a goal: I would read a million words in Spanish and see what my level was afterwards. A million words is about twenty novels, so it was a lot of work.

I started with very easy reading, like transcripts[20] of podcasts[21] for learners. After I had learned some basic things, I started reading translations of books that I knew in English. For example, I have read *Harry Potter* and *Game of Thrones* in English, so I read them in Spanish, too.

Finally, I was ready to read completely new books. I fell in love with Latin American[22] authors such as Isabel Allende, Luis Jorge Borges and Manuel Puig. With the reading, I also listened to podcasts, but I always read the transcripts and counted the words as part of my reading.

After I achieved my goal, I tested myself by writing and talking to native speakers, and found I was at an intermediate level. I could understand almost everything I read, understand clear speech, and have conversations at a comfortable level. And I had spent most my time reading, not speaking!

In one year I learned more than most students learn in five years.

I didn't try to remember the vocabulary and grammar rules. I absorbed[23] them.

By now, you're either thinking, 'I don't believe this!' or you're ready to start reading for hours a day.

But the next thing I'm going to say is extremely important: **you must read books that are easy. You must**

read books that are fun[24]. If a book is too difficult or too boring, put it down and find another one.

Stephen Krashen, an expert in second language acquisition[25], says, 'Only read things in English that are fun and interesting. Read things that are really easy, that you wouldn't read in your native language[26] because they are "too" easy. So you can read comics, magazines, detective stories, romance stories and so on. Don't feel bad about reading translations.'[27]

You should read books so easy that, when you see a word you don't know, you can understand the meaning from context[28]. Research has shown that in order for this to happen, the text needs to be at least 98% words that you already know[29].

'98%? That's so high!'

I know, dear reader. But let me show you an example. Here's a text where I've replaced 10% of the words with nonsense words[30]. So you should understand 90% of the words.

Jerry FLURGED out of bed and opened the curtains. He BIMPED to himself as he made breakfast. He poured coffee and put butter on his POFFER. His phone rang, and he picked it up. He was so shocked by who was TORNGLING that he dropped his VINKY on the floor.

Is that easy to understand? Could you read a whole book of that?

Here's the same text, but with 2% nonsense words. So you should understand 98% of the words:

Jerry jumped out of bed and opened the curtains. He sang to himself as he made breakfast. He poured coffee and put butter on his toast. His phone rang, and he picked it up. He was so shocked by who was calling that he dropped his VINKY on the floor.[31]

How was that?[32] You probably didn't understand everything, but I bet it was more enjoyable to read than the first text. And that's why reading for pleasure is so great: you might not understand everything, but you will understand enough to follow the story, without having to pick up a dictionary!

So if you find that this book is too hard, read the level below. If you find it boring, go read something else. Yes, I'm giving you permission to stop reading my book. I know not everyone likes my writing style, and that's OK. Find what works for you.

As you read, think about the meaning of the stories, and don't worry if you don't understand every single word. Just relax, and try to get lost in the pages. Believe it or not, when we have fun, we learn far better.

The levels of these volumes are based on a system from the University of Cambridge. You might know the levels as A1, A2, B1, B2, C1 and C2, although these books only cover A2-C1. If you're A1 level, you probably need more guided teaching before you start reading, and if you're C2 level, then you can start reading books for native speakers.

If you feel like your reading level is not so strong, I recommend this strategy[33]: start with the beginner level of the book and reread[34] it level by level, going all the way up to advanced. This will let you really absorb the new language and increase the difficulty slowly. There is not a huge difference between the intermediate-level stories and the advanced-level stories, but even rereading the same story twice can be very useful. We need to see new words and phrases many times before our brain can really understand them.

Finally, this book has no exercises in it. I considered adding them after each story, but I just spent ages[35] telling you how important reading for pleasure is. Exercises will just use up time[36] that you could use to read more.

But if you finish this book and find yourself wanting more stories, do go and listen to my podcast, *Easy Stories in English*. I publish a new story every week, with audio[37] and text, and there are over a hundred episodes[38] for you to listen through.

Happy reading and happy learning!

-Ariel Goodbody

THE NORTH WIND AND THE SUN

Nature is a wonderful thing. We have water, which we can drink from, as well as swim and bathe in[1]. We have fire, which lets us cook food and keep warm. We have trees, which give us fruit and wood. All the parts of nature work in harmony[2], allowing us to live on Earth.

In particular, there are two very important parts of nature: the North Wind and the Sun. The North Wind lets us know when the weather is about to change, and the Sun keeps us warm and gives us light.

But the North Wind and the Sun work a bit differently to the other parts of nature. Instead of working in harmony, they always argue over which one is better than the other, and in particular they argue about one thing: what being strong actually means.

The North Wind thinks that strength[3] comes from power. If you have power, you can do what you want, and everyone has to respect you. The North Wind sees how humankind goes to war and kills each other, and there-fore she knows that power is what makes you strong.

'The humans understand,' she says to herself. 'The strongest person is always the leader, and if anyone annoys them, BAM[4]! It's over for them. Strength is power.'

The Sun thinks differently. She thinks that strength comes from kindness[5]. If you are kind, everyone will like you, and in your time of need there will always be a friend there to help you. She sees how humans fall in love with each other, form families and close groups of friends, and therefore she knows that kindness is what makes you strong.

'The humans understand,' the Sun says to herself. 'Even if you are not the leader of a country, the happiest humans are always the kindest. Because when you are kind to the world, the world is kind to you.'

One day, the North Wind and the Sun were having their usual argument.

'You're just a little weakling[6], really,' said the North Wind. 'You have all that sunshine and heat, but you couldn't hurt a fly.'

'I don't need to hurt anyone, thank you very much.'

'You're wrong! What if all the clouds in the sky came to suffocate[7] you? Would you just sit there and die?'

'And why would the clouds attack me? They are my friends.'

'Just imagine! What if it happened? What would your kindness do for you then?'

'That's a stupid question, because it would never happen. I'm not like you, I don't try to make enemies.'

'Ugh[8], I can't stand you!' said the North Wind. 'Fine, since I'm such a good friend, I'll help you understand. See that man down there?'

The Sun looked down at the earth, where a man was walking along a country road. It was winter, and there was a bitter cold[9] in the air, so the man was wrapped tightly in his coat.

'Here's how it will go,' said the North Wind. 'We'll both try to make that man take off his coat. The person who does it first wins. If you win, I'll admit that kindness is what makes you strong. But if *I* win, then you have to agree that power is what makes you strong. Got it?'

The Sun smiled. 'Fine. I will play your game.'

'Me first,' said the North Wind. 'This won't take long.'

The North Wind flew down to the man and blew as hard as she could. The trees started to shake, leaves flew through the air, and all the birds flew away. An icy cold came over the earth[10].

But instead of removing his coat, the man held it tighter. The more the North Wind blew, the colder it got, and the tighter the man held his coat. The North Wind blew and blew, but the man would not take off his coat.

This person is holding their coat tightly because it is cold

'Hmm!' said the North Wind, flying away. 'I tried my

best. If *I* couldn't get him to take it off, you certainly won't be able to. You should give up now.'

The Sun smiled. 'I think it's worth a try.'

She moved out from behind the clouds and bathed the world in light[11]. The trees stopped moving, the birds sat on their branches and sang, and the cold earth warmed up.

As the man walked, he started to sweat[12], and, seeing the Sun shining bright, he took off his coat and hung it over his arm. He walked happily along the road, and it was such lovely weather that he stopped and sat in the shade.

'I don't understand!' cried the North Wind. The Sun had just stood there!

The Sun laughed. 'I told you that strength[13] comes from kindness[14]. Who doesn't love a warm summer's day?'

The North Wind couldn't believe it. 'I still don't agree with you. You were just lucky. This guy liked the sunshine, but that doesn't mean all humans are stupid like that!'

The Sun smiled. 'We don't have to agree on everything, you know. I still love you.'

And the North Wind felt very warm and could say nothing more.

STRANGE FRIENDS

Once upon a time, there were a cat and a mouse who lived together in a little house. The cat did not chase[1] and eat the mouse, like normal cats, which meant that they could be friends. Everyone called them the 'strange friends', and they lived a peaceful life in the city.

One day, the cat came and spoke to the mouse.

'We must think of winter. It is bright and sunny now, but in a few months' time it will be dark and cold, and there will be hardly any food to eat. We should save something for then. After all, if you go out looking for food in the winter, a cat might eat you!'

'You're right,' said the mouse. 'I know what food we should keep. Let's buy a pot of fat[2].'

So they bought a pot of fat, and were about to put it in the kitchen, when the mouse said, 'Wait! We cannot keep it here. If we see it, we will want to eat it. Let us put it somewhere where we will forget about it until we need it. Let us put it in the church, under the altar³.'

So they went into the church, hid the pot of fat under the altar, and then quickly forgot about it.

Or at least, the mouse forgot about it, but the cat thought about the pot of fat very often.

At first she thought, 'Ah, what a wonderful idea it was to get that pot of fat! We will be very thankful⁴ for it in winter.'

But as the weeks passed, she thought more and more about the fat. She dreamt about going and eating the fat. It would taste so good!

So the cat thought of a plan. She came to the mouse and said, 'Dear mouse, I have to ask you a favour. You see, my cousin has given birth to⁵ a beautiful little kitten with white and brown fur. He really is very special, and my cousin has asked me to come to the christening⁶ and be his godmother⁷. Would it be alright if I left you to look after the house alone, just for one day?'

'Of course, of course!' said the mouse. 'Family is the most important thing. Go and enjoy the christening, and if there is some nice food or drink, bring some back to me. In fact, I would love just a few drops of the wine— christening wine is always sweet and delicious.'

The cat smiled and said, 'I'll do my best.'

Of course, the cat was lying. She had no cousin and nobody had asked her to be godmother. She happily walked to the church, pulled out the pot of fat, and opened it.

Oh, it looked so good! The cat licked[8] at it and ate the top of the fat, until she was full.

Then she went for a walk on the roofs of the city. She hoped to find some dessert there, but she didn't, so she lay down in the sun and slept. She dreamt about the pot of fat again and licked her lips.

When she returned home that evening, the mouse said, 'Well, you look like you've had a wonderful time! I suppose it was a good christening, then?'

'Oh yes, the best I've ever been to.'

'And what did they name the child?'

The cat thought for a moment and then said, 'Top-Off.'

'Top-Off!' said the mouse. 'I have never heard such a strange name in my life. Are there other cats in your family with that name?'

'It is a very normal name, thank you very much. You have a godchild[9], don't you? He's called Big Nose, if I remember. That's a stranger name than Top-Off.'

And with that, the conversation was over.

But the cat did not stop thinking about the pot of fat, and a week later, she wanted to eat from it again.

So again, she went to the mouse and said, 'My dear mouse, I'm afraid I must ask for your assistance[10] again. My cousin has quite an active personality, and has already given birth to[11] another child. This one has a white ring around her neck, which is quite rare. They want me to be godmother again, and I cannot say no. Would you look after the house again?'

'No problem, friend! Go and enjoy yourself, and if you

could possibly spare[12] a few drops of that christening wine...'

'Oh, we drank it up so quickly last time! But I will try.'

Of course, the cat did not go to any christening, but to the altar in the church. This time, she ate half the pot of fat.

'Food tastes much better when you don't have to share it with anyone else,' she said to herself.

When she arrived home, the mouse of course asked her, 'What did they name the child this time?'

'Half-Done,' said the cat.

'Half-Done! Are you telling the truth? I have never heard of that name. I don't think you would find it in a single name dictionary in the country!'

'Then perhaps the dictionaries should be changed,' said the cat.

A few days later, the greedy[13] cat got hungry again, and once more dreamt about the fat. Well, if she had already gone this far, why not go further?

'Good things come in threes[14],' announced the cat to the mouse. 'I have been asked to be godmother again. This child is black with white paws[15], which makes it quite a special kitten. I must attend the christening. Will you take care of the house while I'm gone?'

'Top-Off! Half-Done! Those names really do make me think. I wonder what name it will be today?'

'Well you just sit at home and wonder while I go and take part in the christening.'

So the cat headed off to the church. The mouse

cleaned the whole house, while the cat ate the rest of the pot of fat.

'It is so good to finish a meal,' said the cat. She was so full that she had a long sleep on the roof and did not return home until it was late. The mouse asked what they had named the third child.

'You're not going to like this,' said the cat. 'He is called All-Gone.'

'All-Gone!' cried the mouse. 'That is the strangest name of all! I have never heard such a name in my whole life. What could it mean?'

Pondering[16] these questions, the mouse went off to bed.

After that day, the cat's 'cousin' did not have any more children, and there were no more christenings. Winter finally came, and they ran out of food, but the mouse was not put off[17] by this.

'It is a good thing we have that pot of fat!' she said. 'Let's go to the church and enjoy our food.'

'Yes,' said the cat to herself, 'although you could just put your tongue out the window and lick[18] the air. It will have the same result.'

'Hmm, what was that?'

'Oh, nothing! I am simply looking forward to our food.'

But when they arrived at the church, they found the pot empty.

'Oh no!' said the mouse. 'I see what has happened. I thought we were friends, but in fact you have betrayed[19] me! While you were "going to christenings", you were really off eating the fat. First Top-Off, then Half-Done, then—'

'Do not finish,' said the cat. Just the sound of the names evoked memories[20] of the delicious fat, and she was getting *very* hungry. 'If you say another word, I'll—'

'All-Gone!' cried the mouse.

And with that, the cat jumped on her and ate her up.

Because that is the way of the world. Cats eat mice, and cats get fat.

THE VERY HUNGRY DRAGON

A dragon

Once, there was a very hungry dragon called Grella. Every day, she ate five meals. For breakfast she had ten bananas, five fried eggs, and three slices of toast. For her eleven o'clock snack she had twenty chocolate biscuits

and three cups of tea. For lunch she had twenty bowls of soup and thirty loaves of bread. After lunch, she was very tired, so she slept for an hour, and when she woke up

*A loaf (pronunciation **LOFE**; plural **loaves**) of bread*

she had a jar of pickles, because she loved the salty[1] taste. Finally, for supper she had a roast pig covered with honey and herbs.

A pickle

This was all very well and good. After all, Grella was a dragon, and dragons are almost always hungry. But it was strange, because Grella never ate jewels.

'I don't understand!' said Grella's mother. 'Soup and pickles and pig are all good, but you need some jewels! Jewels have important vitamins[2] in them.'

But Grella *hated* jewels. They were hard, and they didn't taste of anything.

A jewel (pronunciation JOO-el)

At every meal, her mother gave her a plate of jewels, but she never ate them. When her mother made her eat them, she hid them in her cheeks and spat them out[3] later. Her mother even tried changing how the jewels looked. She made a tomato out of rubies[4]. She made a cucumber out of emeralds[5]. She made an aubergine out of

An aubergine (pronunciation OH-buh-zheen). In America, they call them 'eggplants'.

amethysts[6]. But Grella smelled each of them, and knew they were not the right food, and threw them on the floor.

One day, Grella's mother got tired of her always saying no.

'Grella, if you don't eat your jewels, then you can't eat anything else.'

She took away the bananas, and the eggs, and the bread and the biscuits and the pickles. She filled every cupboard with fresh, shiny jewels, and for every meal the family had only jewels.

'Now, eat your dinner, Grella.'

Grella looked at the plate of emeralds in front of her.

'I won't.' She flew to her room and shut the door behind her.

For a few days, she continued like this. She hid in her room, ignoring the plates of jewels that her mother left outside her door. She thought that, after a while, her mother would get so worried that she would give up and bring her a nice juicy pig, but the days passed and Grella got more and more hungry.

Finally, she could not stop herself, and one night she crept out[7] into the kitchen.

She picked up an emerald and looked at it. It just looked so *strange*. It looked like something you would decorate your body or your house with. Not something you would *eat*. But all the other dragons in the world ate them…

Grella's stomach rumbled[8]. She put the emerald in her mouth and bit it. She chewed[9] and chewed, until the emerald turned into dust. Then she swallowed[10] it and went, 'Eugh!' It tasted awful, but it dealt with her hunger, so she ate another, and then another.

By the next morning, Grella had eaten all the jewels in the house. Her mother was very happy.

'Wonderful, just wonderful! Wait here, Grella. I'll go out and fetch some more jewels for breakfast.'

Her mother brought three baskets of jewels back with her, stolen from some king's castle. It was enough to feed a whole family for a week, but while her mother went to wake up the rest of the family, Grella ate all three baskets and waited for more.

'Grella!' said her mother. 'You didn't eat all those jewels, did you?'

'I did,' said Grella. 'And I want more. Where's dessert?'

'Those were all the jewels I got!' said her mother. 'Look, I can go and make some toast if you want.'

But Grella could only think about eating jewels. She needed more and she needed bigger, shinier ones. And most importantly[11], she needed them *now*.

Grella ran to the window and jumped off the balcony, flying away.

'Grella, where are you going?!' shouted her mother. 'It's a school day!'

A cart. The man is carrying things on the cart to sell. Cows are pulling the cart.

But Grella didn't hear her. She flew through the air, and in the distance she smelled jewels. She followed the smell, flying over the rough, sharp mountains where they lived, until she found a merchant road[12]. There, down below, was a cart from a faraway[13] land.

And it was heavy with jewels.

Grella's family had taught her to be a good dragon. She knew that it was bad to kill humans, because then they would come and kill dragons. But that didn't mean she couldn't have a bit of fun.

She flew down and pulled the roof off the cart. The human merchants saw her and screamed, running away and leaving their goods. Grella laughed, and picked up the cart in her hand. She emptied it into her mouth, and chewed[14] the jewels into a delicious mix and swallowed[15] them all in one go[16].

Grella understood now. Her mother had been right. Jewels were *amazing*. They made her feel wonderful inside, like there was a party going on inside her stomach.

Grella gave a big, loud burp[17], and flew off to find more food.

Grella went wild for a whole week, flying round the whole world and stealing all kinds of jewels. People soon found out about her behaviour. Young dragons started stealing thousands of jewels from humans. Of course, all the adult dragons disagreed with this behaviour. Grella was giving them a bad reputation[18] and putting herself in danger. Besides, she should really be in school!

Finally, after eating so many jewels, she grew fat and heavy, and feeling satisfied, she flew home to take a nice, long sleep.

But her mother had different ideas.

'Grella, HOW DARE YOU[19]?!'

'Didn't you *want* me to eat jewels?'

'I— I— Not like *this*! I've been so worried about you, and besides, now everyone is talking about our family and saying nasty things. It was very bad of you!'

Grella's mother kept shouting, but Grella didn't listen to her. She suddenly felt very tired, and she couldn't stop herself from closing her eyes...

When she woke up, it was night. She had no idea how long she had been asleep, but she was sure it had been a very long time. She knew this because her stomach was rumbling[20], which meant it was time to go and eat some jewels.

Grella went to the kitchen and opened the fridge.

No jewels there.

So she went and opened the cupboards.

No jewels there, either.

She looked in the freezer.

No jewels there!

She searched the whole house, and even crept[21] into her parents' bedroom to look around while they were asleep, but she couldn't find a single jewel anywhere!

She did find something in her brother's room, though. Under the bed he had a secret collection. He hated the diet their mother had put them on, and he had hidden away lots of human food: pickles and biscuits and chocolate and bread and tins of all sorts of soup. Grella pulled the food out, put it on the kitchen table and looked at it.

They didn't shine like jewels. They had funny smells. Some were hard, but some were really soft. They had all sorts of different colours. Slowly, she picked up a chocolate biscuit and tried it.

Oh, how she had missed that taste!

Grella started to eat, and by the time her parents woke up, she had eaten almost everything. She lay down on the floor and gave a big, happy burp[22].

'Oh, my daughter!' cried her mother. 'My daughter is back!'

She went and hugged Grella, and the young dragon felt a bit sick.

'I don't understand you!' she said, annoyed. 'First you want me to eat jewels, then you shout at me for it, and now you're happy that I'm eating other food!'

'I know, I know. I'm sorry. I should have never made you change.'

She started crying, and hugged Grella again. Mothers were so confusing!

'My food!' cried Grella's brother. 'Grella, how could you?!'

'Don't worry,' said their mother, drying her eyes. 'From now on, we will have *all* kinds of food in this house. There will be jewels for those who want them, and human food as well.'

And so everything went back to normal. Every day, Grella ate five meals. For breakfast she had ten bananas, five fried eggs, and three slices of toast. For her eleven o'clock snack she had twenty chocolate biscuits and three cups of tea. For lunch she had twenty bowls of soup and thirty loaves of bread. After lunch, she was very tired, so she slept for an hour, and when she woke up she had a jar of pickles, because she loved the salty[23] taste. Finally, for supper she had a roast pig covered with honey and herbs.

Oh, and she still ate jewels sometimes, just for variety.

DOGGO AND KITTY DO THEIR
LAUNDRY

Once, there was a dog and cat, called Doggo and Kitty. Doggo was a very handsome dog. He had long, thick fur that brushed along the floor. Kitty was a charming and gorgeous cat. She had soft, thin fur that felt like silk. The pair of them lived together in a little cottage next to a forest, and they got on very well.

Although Doggo and Kitty were only small little creatures, they had big dreams. They wanted to be like the Big People: the adults. Oh, how wonderful that would be! If only they could walk like adults, talk like adults, and live complicated lives like adults.

But it could not be so. Adults have hands, and Doggo and Kitty only had paws which were big and clumsy[1]. Instead of fingers, they only had sharp claws, which made it very difficult to do things as the adults did.

But Doggo and Kitty worked their hardest to be like the Big People. Perhaps you are wondering: if Doggo and

A paw (animal hand) with sharp claws (they can hurt you!)

Kitty weren't adults, did they go to school? The answer is no, of course. School is not for animals, but for children. Naturally[2], there was no way they could go to school, but they didn't mind this, because school seemed quite boring, anyway.

As I said, Doggo and Kitty lived in a little cottage, which was made of smooth wood and had a pretty red roof. The inside, however, was not so tidy, as Doggo and Kitty had to clean the house with only their clumsy paws, so things got messy very quickly. Also, they hated cleaning, so they didn't do it very often.

One day, Doggo and Kitty were looking for clothes to wear. They loved wearing shirts and trousers and hats, as it made them feel like adults. But there was not a single piece of clothing[3] to be found! Their clothes were not in the drawers, not in the cupboards, and not on the hooks.

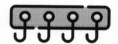

Hooks to put coats on

'What is going on, Kitty?' said Doggo. 'I think a clothes thief has snuck[4] into our house in the night and stolen all our clothes!'

'Not a clothes thief,' said Kitty, 'but a clothes *monster*. Oh, and I am so afraid of monsters!'

'Don't worry, Kitty!' said Doggo. 'I've found them.'

Their clothes were lying on the floor, in a great dirty pile.

'Well, this can't be,' said Doggo, scratching[5] his head. 'Our clothes are all dirty, and no adult wears dirty clothes.'

'You're absolutely right, Doggo,' said Kitty.

'So we will have to burn them and buy new ones,' said Doggo.

'No!' said Kitty. 'We should *wash* them.'

'Ah, yes!' said Doggo. 'The adults have a word for that, don't they? They call it "laundry[6]".'

'Exactly,' said Kitty, and then got very excited. 'We are going to do our laundry, just like the adults do!'

'Fantastic!' said Doggo. 'But, er, how exactly *do* adults do laundry?'

A woman using a washing board

'Oh, it's quite simple,' said Kitty seriously. 'You go and fetch some water, and I'll go get the soap and the washing board.'

'Alright then!' said Doggo.

So Doggo carried a bucket outside to the river and filled it with water. Meanwhile, Kitty searched through the kitchen cupboards. She found many strange things: toothpaste, lipstick[7] and even buttons.

After all, the kitchen was the place for things that you put in or on your mouth, and Kitty liked to chew[8] on buttons. Finally she found what she was looking for: a round, red bar of soap that shone[9] in the light. She carefully put it on the table and then went off to find the washing board.

When Doggo came back inside, sweating[10] from the heavy bucket, he saw something on the table. He dropped the bucket and went to look at it. It was round and red and shone in the light.

Well, thought Doggo, *since we are in the kitchen, this must be something to put in or on my mouth. And it looks very tasty!*

And what do you do with tasty things? Why, you eat them, of course!

So Doggo put the red thing in his mouth and bit down on it.

But, oh! Eugh! Argh! It was not tasty at all! In fact, it was *disgusting*!

'Eugh!' cried Doggo, spitting out[11] the soap. 'This is horrible!'

As he coughed and spat, his mouth filled up with foam. The more he coughed, the more foam there was, until there was foam coming out of his mouth and nose. Just then, Kitty came back into the kitchen.

'Doggo, dear Doggo!' she said. 'What is the matter? There's so much foam coming out of you, you look like a fountain! Are you sick?'

*Foam (pronunciation **FOME**) coming out of a bottle of Coke*

'No!' coughed Doggo. 'I'm not sick. I found this red thing here, and I thought it looked tasty, like a piece of cheese, or maybe some sweets. So I ate it, but *pagh*! It was a nasty, horrible thing, something that should *not* be in a kitchen, and now my mouth is full of foam!'

'Doggo!' said Kitty. 'That wasn't food at all. It was *soap*! It was the soap for the laundry!'

'So that's why it tasted so bad!' said Doggo. 'Why was it in the kitchen?'

'Well, one time, one of the children told me that he'd been very naughty[12]. His mother said, "Oh, you awful boy! If you do that again I'll wash your mouth out with soap!" I'd never thought that soap was something to put in your mouth. I definitely think it's a bad idea now. But after I heard the boy say that, I put the soap in here.'

'Oh!' said Doggo, jumping up. 'You mean the adults put soap in their mouths, too? Well then, I was just being mature[13], Kitty.'

'Anyway,' said Kitty, 'I will go and fetch another bar of soap, and you will *not* eat this one, understand? Now go and get some water and wash out your mouth.'

'Yes, Kitty,' said Doggo.

So Doggo went and washed out his mouth with water from the bucket. Then he went and fetched more water. By the time he had returned, Kitty was standing with the washing board and a fresh bar of soap. They were all ready to do their laundry, except one thing was still missing.

'Wait, Kitty!' said Doggo. 'We don't have a brush. How can we do our laundry without a brush?'

'That's a good question,' said Kitty. 'Without a brush, we won't be able to rub[14] our clothes, like the adults do.'

'Hmm,' said Doggo.

They sat down for a while and considered the problem. Then Kitty leapt[15] in the air.

'Doggo, I have the perfect solution! Brushes have long, thick hair. And *you* have long, thick fur. We'll use you as a brush!'

'What a fantastic idea!' said Doggo.

So Kitty sat down with the washing board, the bucket of water, and Doggo. She threw some dirty clothes onto the washing board, wet the soap[16] in the bucket, and rubbed the clothes. Then she picked up Doggo and rubbed him on the clothes, until they disappeared under a mountain of foam. Finally, she dipped[17] them in the water and washed the foam away.

Afterwards, they had a pile of clean, wet clothes, and a very dirty, wet Doggo.

'Kitty,' said Doggo, 'I have discovered a small problem in our plan. We don't have a towel to dry the clothes with, and I'm far too wet to use.'

'Hmm,' said Kitty.

They sat down for a while and considered the problem. Then Doggo leapt[18] in the air.

'Kitty, I have the perfect solution! Towels have soft, thin hair. And *you* have soft, thin fur. We'll use you as a towel!'

'What a fantastic idea!' said Kitty.

So Doggo sat down with the pile of clothes and Kitty. He threw the clothes on the washing board and dried them using Kitty.

Afterwards, they had a pile of clean, dry clothes. But Doggo and Kitty were dripping wet[19] and very dirty.

'Doggo,' said Kitty, 'if an adult saw us now, they would be shocked! We have finished our laundry, but now we must wash *ourselves*!'

'Alright then, Kitty,' said Doggo. 'I'll wash you, and then you wash me.'

So Kitty climbed onto the washing board and Doggo rubbed her with soap. She shouted 'Ow!' and 'Oof!' because Doggo rubbed her hard and his claws were very sharp. When Doggo was finished, it was his turn, and he climbed onto the washing board. Once again, she rubbed him with soap, and he shouted 'Ow!' and 'Oof!' because she rubbed him just as hard as he had rubbed her, and her claws were just as sharp.

Finally, they stood up and squeezed[20] each other, letting out all the water onto the floor.

'Simple,' said Kitty. 'Now we just need to hang ourselves up to dry, just like the adults do with laundry.'

'Aha!' said Doggo. 'So that's what the washing line is for. I thought it was for swinging[21] on.'

They went into the garden, where the washing line hung between the house and a big tree. They climbed up the tree and onto the line, and they hung off it by their claws. The sun shone bright and warm.

Clothes on a washing line

'The sun is shining on us, Doggo!' said Kitty. 'We'll be dry in no time flat[22].'

But as soon as she said the words, a huge raincloud[23] came, and it started pouring down.

'It's raining!' shouted Doggo. 'Our laundry is getting wet! We must take it down!'

Quickly, they leapt off the washing line and ran inside the house.

'Is it still raining?' asked Kitty, looking out the door.

'It's stopped,' said Doggo, 'so let's hang up our laundry again.'

Once more, they climbed up the tree and onto the washing line. The sun shone on them, and they would be dry in no time flat!

But then the raincloud returned.

'It's raining!' shouted Kitty. 'Our laundry is getting wet! We must take it down!'

Quickly, they leapt off the washing line and ran inside the house. Then the sun came back out, so they ran outside, but then it started raining again, so they ran back inside. They hung from the washing line, ran inside, and returned to the washing line until it was evening, and the sun had stopped shining.

By now, they were both clean and dry, but very, very tired.

'Our laundry is done!' said Doggo.

They had forgotten about the actual laundry[24], which lay in a wet pile on the floor.

'What a day!' said Kitty. 'But Doggo, we did our laundry! We're one step closer[25] to being adults!'

'There's nothing more to do than go to bed,' said Doggo.

And with the satisfaction[26] of a hard day's work, they climbed upstairs and into their beds and quickly fell asleep.

DOGGO AND KITTY TEAR THEIR TROUSERS

Once, there was a dog and cat, called Doggo and Kitty. Doggo was a very handsome dog, and Kitty was a charming and gorgeous cat. The pair of them lived together in a little cottage next to a forest, and they got on very well.

We have seen how Doggo and Kitty did their laundry[1], so we now know that Doggo and Kitty are *very* good at doing the housework. And there were always so many things to do! But the day after they did their laundry was Sunday, and Sunday is a day of rest.

That morning, Doggo looked through the window and saw that the sun was shining bright and cheerful. 'Kitty!' he said. 'It is a gorgeous day. Let's take advantage of the sunshine and go to the forest. What else could one do on a day like this?'

'I completely agree,' said Kitty. 'And what luck! We

have done our laundry, and now we can wear our nice clean clothes to go out.'

So they dressed up in their finest clothes[2] and went outside.

'Oh, how I wish I had a parasol[3]!' said Kitty. 'The bright sun hurts my eyes, and I would be a pretty little kitty with a parasol. I am sure *nobody* has seen such a pretty kitty before!'

'There's nothing wrong with getting a bit of sun,' said Doggo. 'We've been stuck inside[4] all winter, and you look quite white. Yes, some sun will be good for you!'

And Doggo was right. During the winter, they sat by the fire and played games, and some days they didn't see the sun at all.

This dog's ears are uneven, not even. One is up and the other is down.

'Well,' said Kitty, 'you should see how *you* look. Your ears are completely uneven, one sticking up and one hanging down! You can't walk around with uneven ears.'

'Oh dear!' said Doggo. 'Thank you for letting me know, Kitty.'

Doggo adjusted[5] his ears and they continued on their way. While they walked, they spoke about what they would do in the forest. Oh, what fun they would have! They were going to play hide-and-seek[6], which was Kitty's favourite game, because

Doggo always lost. He would hide in a bush[7] or a tree, but his ears always stuck out[8], and he was easy to find.

As they walked, they came past a bush with a rabbit inside. When the rabbit turned and saw Doggo, he started laughing.

'Haha,' said the rabbit, 'look at that silly dog! He has one ear sticking up and the other hanging down. Just like this.' And the rabbit moved his ears to look like Doggo's. Doggo checked his ears, and found that they were uneven again.

'That nasty little rabbit is laughing at you!' cried Kitty.

Doggo got angry and ran after the rabbit. He jumped into the bush, but the rabbit was much faster than him, and easily ran away.

'Oh, there are so many thorns in this bush!' cried Doggo, pulling some out of his paws[9]. 'It was a stupid idea to run after that rabbit.'

'Those thorns didn't really hurt you, did they?' said Kitty.

'No, not really,' said Doggo.

Doggo adjusted[10] his ears and they continued on their way. A few minutes later, they met the children who lived on the other side of the forest.

There are thorns on this rose. They are sharp and can hurt you.

'Hello, Doggo and Kitty!' said the children. 'Since it's such a lovely sunny day, we all decided to go for a stroll[11] in the forest.'

'We had the same idea!' said Kitty.

'You're both dressed up very nice!' said the children. 'But, oh no!'

They started giggling[12]. Doggo quickly checked his ears, but they were even, so why were they laughing?

'Look, boys! Look, girls! Doggo has torn[13] his trousers!'

'What?!' said Doggo. 'Kitty, the *dear* children say that I have a tear in my trousers. Could you look and see?' Doggo didn't want to look himself, in case he tore them even more.

So Kitty looked at Doggo's trousers, and then said, 'I'm afraid it's true, Doggo. Your trousers have a big tear in them.'

A needle and thread. You use them to make clothes.

'I bet that happened when I ran into that bush with all those thorns!' said Doggo. 'Oh, I can't believe I've torn my nicest trousers. What a shame! But Kitty, perhaps you have a needle and thread?'

'I'm afraid I don't. But don't worry, Doggo. I'm sure we'll find something on the way, a piece of string or something like that.'

So they said goodbye to the children, who were still laughing and pointing at Doggo, and continued on their way.

String

'Hey, take a look over there!' said Doggo. 'I see something.'

A worm

There, lying on the ground, was a little worm, sleeping in the afternoon sun. It was quite happy, lying in the sunlight, and it thought that nobody could see it, because it was so small. But Doggo saw it.

'It's something long, thin and straight,' said Doggo. 'I think it's a pencil!'

Hearing Doggo's loud voice, the worm woke up. When it saw the huge dog standing over it, it was very afraid, and curled up into a circle.

'No, Doggo, that's no pencil!' said Kitty. 'Pencils can't curl up into a circle. It must be a piece of string. What luck! I can use it to mend your trousers.'

When you curl up, you move into this shape.

A knot
(pronunciation **NOT**)

And with that, Kitty picked up the worm and tied it in a knot to close the tear in Doggo's trousers. The worm could do nothing to stop her.

'Fantastic,' said Doggo. 'Now nobody can laugh at me.'

They continued on their way and spoke about all the places they would hide in later, when they played hide-and-seek[14]. The worm listened and waited, and said to itself, 'I'm no piece of string! I'm a lovely little worm.' And it slowly started to untie the knot[15].

Meanwhile, Doggo and Kitty met one of their friends, Clucky the chicken.

'Hello, Clucky!' said Doggo and Kitty.

'Hello, Doggo and Kitty. Doggo, look out! There is something on your leg. Ooh, it's a worm!'

Because she was a chicken, Clucky *loved* to eat worms, so she pecked[16] at Doggo's leg and tried to eat it. Luckily for the worm, it had just finished untying the knot, and it fell off and ran away before Clucky could catch it.

'How unusual,' said Clucky. 'It was climbing out of a hole in your trousers, like it was eating them. I didn't know worms ate trousers. It's a shame I couldn't catch it.'

'Yes, what a shame!' said Doggo. But secretly, he was glad that Clucky hadn't caught the worm, as he hated violence[17].

'Oh, Doggo!' said Kitty, looking at his trousers again. 'Once again your lovely trousers are torn. That thing was not a worm, but the string I used to mend them!'

'No way,' said Clucky. 'That was a worm, no doubt. String doesn't curl up like that! But don't worry, Doggo. I can't mend your trousers myself, but if you follow this path, you'll come to a house where a seamstress[18] lives. She can mend your trousers for you.'

So they said goodbye to Clucky and continued on their way to the seamstress's house.

When she saw Doggo's trousers, she was surprised.

'Wow, that's a big tear!' said the seamstress. 'But

Sunday is a day of rest, so I don't really feel like working. I have an idea. If you help me with a problem, I'll mend your trousers for you. See, a family of mice has moved into my kitchen, and they're quite annoying. They always steal my food. If you get rid of them, I'll mend your trousers. *But*, you can't drink the milk or eat the biscuits on the table! Those are for me.'

Doggo and Kitty agreed to catch the mice and promised to leave the milk and biscuits. The seamstress showed them to the kitchen, and all the mice ran away and hid in their holes.

'Here's the plan,' said Kitty. 'I'll go outside, and you stand in front of their holes, Doggo.'

So Doggo stood guard[19] outside the mice's holes. Kitty went outside and said, 'Yay! There's a dog inside with one ear sticking up and the other hanging down, and he has a big tear in his trousers. How funny he looks! You can't help but laugh at him!'

The mice, who loved nothing more than a good laugh, ran out of their holes to see this dog. And then, of course, Doggo jumped on them and caught them under his paw[20].

'Oh no!' cried the mice. 'Are you going to eat us? Oh, you do look so silly, but it's not worth dying for!'

'You're very lucky,' said Doggo. 'I hate violence[21]. But you must leave the seamstress's house and never come back!'

The mice promised to never return and ran away, giggling[22] about Doggo's trousers.

'Fantastic work!' said the seamstress, coming back into

the kitchen. 'A little unusual, but it got the job done[23]. Now, let me have a look at those trousers.'

So the seamstress mended the tear in Doggo's trousers, and then she invited them to stay for milk and biscuits, and Doggo and Kitty couldn't say no to that, could they? The biscuits were quite delicious.

Afterwards, they walked home through the forest. In the end, they were too tired to play hide-and-seek, but they slept very well, although Doggo's ears were uneven throughout the night[24].

DOGGO AND KITTY BAKE A CAKE

Once, there was a dog and cat, called Doggo and Kitty. Doggo was a very handsome dog, and Kitty was a charming and gorgeous cat. The pair of them lived together in a little cottage next to a forest, and they got on very well.

One day, Kitty looked at their calendar. It was five years out of date, but Kitty saw no reason to change it, because the years didn't change, did they?

'Doggo!' said Kitty. 'According to the calendar, today is my birthday.'

'Yay!' said Doggo. 'Birthdays are a wonderful occasion. We will have to celebrate. But how? I have never celebrated a birthday before.'

Kitty was sure that they *had* celebrated a birthday before, since they happened every year. But she wasn't certain, and she didn't want to sound stupid, so she said nothing.

'Yes, we must celebrate!' said Kitty. 'We'll have to think of the most wonderful way to celebrate the most important birthday!'

While Doggo and Kitty pondered[1] the issue, so did another group of people: the children who lived on the other side of the forest. They adored[2] Doggo and Kitty, but they missed Kitty's birthday last year, so this year they planned on surprising her with a cake.

The problem was, they didn't have the ingredients for a cake and they didn't know how to actually bake one. They had no flour, milk and eggs, and they didn't even realise that you needed those for a good cake! After all, when you see a finished cake, you don't see the flour, milk and eggs. So they used whatever they had around and made their own recipe.

First, they found a battered[3] old cake tin, which they would bake the cake in. Then they took some sand from the sandpit[4] in the garden and poured it into the tin, because the best cakes were always soft, like sand.

A cake tin and a cake

Still, it couldn't be too soft, so they poured in some water and mixed it with the sand, getting plenty of water and sand on the floor as they did so.

Now they had a lovely brown cake, which only needed decoration[5] to be perfect. So they took some small, white stones from the garden and put them on top of it, because nice cakes always had nuts and things like that on top. Finally, they put the cake tin in the oven and waited for an hour, although the oven wasn't switched on, because only their parents were allowed to do that.

Nuts

Out of the oven came a wonderful cake! The children said, 'Wow!' and really wanted to try it, but they knew that would be unfair. It was Kitty's cake, after all! So they carried it through the forest to the wooden cottage where Doggo and Kitty lived.

'Hello, Doggo and Kitty!' the children said. 'We baked you a cake and brought it here as a surprise for Kitty's birthday.'

'A surprise!' said Kitty. 'How wonderful. We were pondering[6] how to celebrate, and this is perfect!'

'The cake tastes divine[7],' said the children, copying the word their parents always used. 'You're going to love it.'

'Well then!' said Doggo. 'Come into the kitchen and we'll sit down to eat.'

But when they saw the cake, Doggo and Kitty realised that the cake was awful. The soft cake was actually sand, and the delicious nuts were actually stones. Nobody could eat such a cake, but Doggo and Kitty adored[8] the children, so they cut up the cake and served the slices.

'You first, Doggo,' said Kitty. 'You're the oldest, so you get to eat first.'

'Oh no, I couldn't!' said Doggo. 'It's *your* birthday. You should eat first!'

So Kitty held the slice of cake up to her nose and

smelled it. It really smelled quite horrible, like wet earth, so Kitty moved her lips, pretending[9] to eat it.

'Yum yum!' she said. 'Oh, it's such a delicious cake, I don't think I could eat any more!'

Doggo and the children soon understood the game. They all held up their slices, smelled them and said, 'Yum yum!' and then put them down again.

'Thank you so much, children,' said Kitty, glad she hadn't actually had to eat the cake. 'We've never had such a lovely cake before.'

The children laughed, said goodbye and headed home. Doggo and Kitty took the plates of cake to the river outside and threw them into the water.

'How nice of the children to do that for us,' said Doggo, 'but really, who could eat such an awful cake? Still, I am now very hungry for a *real* cake.'

'Me too,' said Kitty, her stomach rumbling[10]. 'Well, since it's my birthday, why don't we bake one? Although I don't actually know *how* to bake a cake.'

'I know, I know!' said Doggo, his tail wagging[11]. 'It's really quite easy, Kitty. All you have to do is add your favourite food to the cake. If you add five delicious foods, then the cake will be five times as[12] good. If you add ten delicious foods, then the cake will be ten times as good.'

'What if we add a hundred delicious things?' said Kitty.

'Uh, I can't count that high!' said Doggo. 'Maybe... a hundred times as good? Wow, that cake would taste really amazing!'

'Oh, this is marvelous!' said Kitty. 'We're going to make the most delicious cake ever!'

So Doggo and Kitty took out their cake tin and got to cooking.

First, they took flour, milk and eggs out of the cupboard and poured them into the bowl. Unlike[13] the children, they had the basic ingredients, although they threw the eggs into the bowl with the shells[14] on them! Then they mixed until it was soft.

'Now what do we do?' asked Kitty.

'Now we add all our favourite things!' said Doggo. 'What kind of cake do you want to make?'

'Hmm,' said Kitty, 'well, above all, it must be sweet.'

So she poured a kilogram of sugar into the bowl.

'But not just sweet!' said Doggo. 'The Big People always like to have "balanced[15] flavours".'

So he poured a kilogram of salt into the bowl, to make it even.

'And let's add some butter and jam,' said Kitty, 'since we always have that for breakfast.'

'*You* have jam,' said Doggo, 'but I like cheese on my bread. So let's add that instead.'

'Fine, fine,' said Kitty, 'but we need something greasy[16], too. How about bacon?'

'Perfect!' said Doggo. 'And let's not forget nuts. I really was looking forward to having the nuts on the children's cake, until I realised they were stones.'

'Nuts are fine,' said Kitty, 'but remember, Doggo! Balanced flavours! Let's have some cucumber, too.'

'And bones!' said Doggo, jumping and wagging his tail[17] in excitement. 'Oh, I can't eat a cake without bones! They're the best thing in the world!'

'Maybe for *you*,' said Kitty. 'But fine, if you're adding bones, I'm adding mice.'

'Oh,' said Doggo, 'if we're adding meat, throw in a few sausages, too.'

'And finally, cream!' said Kitty. 'Every good dessert has cream in it!'

'Fantastic thinking,' said Doggo, 'and I think that would go well with a bit of garlic.'

'And chocolate,' said Kitty.

So they added all their favourite foods to the bowl, which was all the food they had in the house. They mixed and mixed, sweating[18] over the mountain of food in the bowl, until it was soft.

'Phew[19]!' said Doggo. 'This is going to be an excellent cake. All we have to do now is bake it.'

So they carried the massive[20] cake to the oven, careful not to drop it, and pushed it inside. Unlike[21] the children, they were allowed to switch the oven on, so their cake actually baked. While they waited, they went and played cards in the other room. When the cake was done, they took it out and put it on the table.

'Oh, what a handsome cake!' said Doggo.

'Not "handsome", Doggo,' said Kitty. 'Pretty! But we can't eat it yet, or we'll burn our mouths. We have to let it cool[22].'

So they opened the window and put the cake on the windowsill[23].

'Hmm,' said Kitty, 'since the children brought us a cake, I think we should do the same. But I don't want to carry it all the way through the forest.'

'No problem,' said Doggo. 'We'll invite them over here again.'

So they walked through the forest, very excited about their baking success, all the way to the children's house.

But while they were away, a very naughty[24] dog passed by the wooden cottage. The smell of the cake came towards him, and his stomach rumbled[25] like a lorry.

'Wow!' he said. 'I've never smelt something so delicious before. It's like somebody mixed together a hundred delicious foods into one! I must find it.'

He followed the smell until he found the cottage and saw the cake cooling[26]. Oh, the cake looked as good as it smelled! The dog's eyes and mouth began to water[27].

So the dog jumped onto the windowsill and ate the cake. The rumbling in his stomach went quiet, and he went to the river and drank lots of water. Then, feeling tired and satisfied, he sat down by a big tree.

Except he *didn't* feel satisfied. The cake had tasted so good going in, but in his stomach it felt so *bad*. It felt like he'd eaten a hundred sticks and stones, or like there was a fire inside him!

'Oof! Ow! Just what was in that cake?' the dog asked himself.

When Doggo and Kitty returned with the children, they were shocked to find the cake gone.

'Oh, no!' said Kitty. 'I am so sorry, children. I don't know what happened!'

'I think I know!' said one of the children.

He pointed to the river, where the naughty[28] dog was sitting by a tree.

'That dog has a massive[29] stomach. *He* must have eaten the cake!'

The naughty dog would've gotten up and run away, but he was in too much pain.

'I'm sorry,' he said. 'It smelt so good, and looked so delicious, and I just couldn't stop myself! But oh, how I regret it!'

'Don't worry,' said Kitty. 'Looking at you, I don't think the cake was very nice, anyway. I have quite a delicate[30] stomach, so I'm glad you ate it instead of us!'

'Well, I'm not glad!' cried the dog, and they all laughed.

'But there's just one problem,' said Doggo. 'We were going to have that cake for dinner, and we put all of the food in the house into it. Now we have nothing to eat, and I'm so hungry!'

'Not to worry, Doggo and Kitty,' said the children. 'Come and eat dinner at our house. We'll make mud[31] pie for dessert!'

So Doggo and Kitty followed the children back through the forest to have dinner at their house. Luckily, their parents cooked, and made a lovely dinner of soup, chicken and bones. Doggo and Kitty were very happy to be able to eat with some of the Big People, and the food was delicious, too. Much better than sand cake and mud pie! Still, they didn't want to be rude, so they pretended[32] to eat the children's mud pie.

And the naughty dog? Well, he was in so much pain he couldn't move an inch[33], and he sat up all night, crying as his stomach rumbled. But he learned his lesson[34]. He would never steal from Doggo and Kitty again!

SLEEPING BEAUTY

A fairy is a girl with wings who can use magic

In a world far away from ours, there were two castles: the Blue Castle and the Red Castle. In the Blue Castle, where the fairies lived, everything was soft and as blue as a clear sky. Joy[1] grew there, even when misery[2] grew too.

Among the fairies, the most beautiful was a young creature called Izod. Izod loved her people, and her people loved her. She had a heart as soft as butter, and seeing anything unfair made her cry. Whenever one of the High Fairies passed away, she cried for months longer than anyone else. Her wings were as beautiful as her heart was soft. They were longer and paler[3] than the wings of any other fairy. They shone[4] in the sunlight[5] and danced in the air as she flew, and everyone called them her 'wings of water'.

Nobody was surprised when Izod was chosen to be the next queen. She was loved by all, and the leader of the Blue Castle was always a fairy with a great heart. At first, Izod was scared, but as the years passed, her excitement grew. On her sixteenth birthday, she would become queen, and she would be able to share all her love with all the people.

But on the day of her sixteenth birthday, the men from the Red Castle came.

Their eyes burned like fire, and they dyed[6] the Blue Castle red with blood. They murdered without care, and for every drop of blood that fell, Izod cried a tear. When they finally came to her, her home was all fire, and her body was a dry, empty shell[7].

But the Red Men did not kill her. That would have been too kind for a fairy like Izod. They beat her, pulled out her wings, and left her alone in the Blue Castle. All alone.

Her beauty was dead, and her magic was gone.

Della loved her people, and her people loved her. Her mother and father, the King and Queen of the Red Castle, always spoke about how wonderful she was, and her people gave her many gifts and compliments[8]. She had gorgeous red hair, which burned bright in the sun, and the people called it her 'hair of fire'.

In the Red Castle, everything was warm, bright and

strong, and Della was the strongest of all. She watched many battles between gladiators[9] without fear, and when they killed each other, she jumped and cheered[10]. She would be queen one day, and she would be a powerful queen.

But on Della's sixteenth birthday, everything changed.

The day started with beautiful sunshine but quickly turned dark and wet. Many people had come to celebrate the Princess's birthday, and now they stood inside the cold castle. It was a bad sign, said some, but the King and Queen laughed at their comments.

'The gods are afraid of you, because you are so strong,' said the King. 'Even they want to challenge you.'

Della smiled. 'One day, I will destroy them, too.'

Della sat on the throne[11] and received the people's gifts: cakes, jewellery, gorgeous paintings and dresses, but also a wide range of weapons[12], and even a few war horses. Finally, Sir Galen, the head of the Queen's guards, came up, dressed in his autumn-leaf uniform. He had a very interesting present for Della.

'These are fairy wings. They have strong magic. Although magic is dangerous, a strong queen must learn to control it. Be careful with them.'

Della examined[13] the wings, but as soon as she touched them, the doors to the Red Castle flew open. A terrible wind blew and heavy rain came inside, bringing angry cries from the guests.

'Shut those doors!' said the Queen.

The guards attempted to do so, but the doors were

held open by the wind. Out of the
rain stepped a tall figure[14] in a black
cloak. As soon as they were inside,
the doors shut behind them. All stood
in silence and watched the strange
figure, who pushed through the
crowd towards the Princess.

'Who are you?' demanded the
Queen.

*A cloak (pronunciation **CLOKE**) is a big piece of clothing that you wear outside*

The figure stopped and showed
her face. It was a woman, but no
ordinary woman. Her skin was dark blue, she had deep
wrinkles[15], and her eyes were as white as milk. Despite
this, she looked soft, but also very sad. She looked like a
raincloud[16].

Della had heard of the Blue Castle and the strange blue
fairies who lived there, but they had all died, many years
ago. That was what her parents had told her.

The blue woman raised a thin finger and pointed at
Della. 'Those wings are mine. Return them to me.'

Her voice came out as a dry whisper[17], but nobody else
said a word as she spoke. For the first time in her life,
Della felt fear, true fear.

'These are not your wings!' she cried. 'Sir Galen gave
them to me.'

The blue woman repeated herself. 'Those wings are
mine. Return them to me. I need them to fly.'

'Guards!' shouted the King. 'Take this woman!'

But the guards didn't move. Nobody in the room

moved. Everyone was under some kind of spell[18], apart from the fairy and the Princess.

The blue woman repeated, stronger this time, 'Return my wings to me! I need them to fly.' She sounded like she might burst into tears.

Della calmly[19] stood up, taking the wings in her hands. She held them up to the light and examined[20] them. They were a beautiful piece of work[21], too complicated to be a work of nature, but at the same time, too delicate[22] to be the work of a human.

Della never usually gave things up. That was how her parents had taught her. And yet, she had a strange feeling in the bottom of her stomach. She knew that if she did not return the wings to this woman, her birthday would be ruined[23].

All eyes on her, Della went down the steps and went towards the fairy.

'No!' shouted Sir Galen. 'It is Izod, the bad fairy of the Blue Castle!'

Della stopped suddenly. The fairy's face became angry. She jumped towards the wings, and her spell was broken[24]. The guards ran forward, grabbing her thin arms and easily holding her back.

'If she will not give me my wings, then let her suffer[25] like me! If I cannot fly, then she must sleep. Tonight, your dear princess will fall into a deep sleep and never wake up again!'

And then she was gone, her wet cloak falling to the floor. The Red Castle was silent, and the rain outside stopped, the sun finally returning. But nobody could feel its warmth[26].

Although the people of the Red Castle looked down on[27] magic, they understood its power. They believed the words of the blue fairy, and the King and Queen asked for the help of the best healers[28] in the country to remove the spell.

But nobody could do it, because it was a magic more powerful than any of them had ever seen. All they could do was try to stop Della from sleeping.

So that night, Della did not go to bed. She didn't go to bed the night after, either. For a whole week, she avoided her bed, and tried to stay awake however she could. Her parents found entertainers[29]—musicians, clowns and dancers—to keep her busy every minute of the night.

And yet, with each passing day, Della grew more tired, and her parents could do nothing about it. One night, at dinner, her head fell onto her plate and she fell asleep.

The King and Queen tried to wake her up. They shook her. They held sweet-smelling flowers and horrible-smelling drinks in front of her nose. The musicians played as loud as they could. They held her nose and poured buckets of water over her. But the Princess did not move, and finally, exhausted and sad, they carried her to bed. They sat by her every night, telling stories and brushing her hair[30]. But finally, their suffering grew too much, and even they left her.

Della lay alone in her room. She was a sleeping beauty, and nothing more.

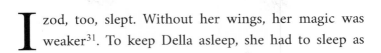

I zod, too, slept. Without her wings, her magic was weaker[31]. To keep Della asleep, she had to sleep as well.

In their dreams, the two girls met. At first, Della ran away at the sight of the fairy, escaping into the dream world. But as the years passed, she realised that they would have to talk in the end. So she sat down by the sea and waited, and eventually Izod came to her.

'Why did you do this?' Della asked. She no longer sounded like a proud child. She was a suffering woman now, just like Izod.

'I had nothing left.'

Della shook her head. 'But what did you gain from this? Now we are both asleep. You do not have your wings, and I will never be queen. Does it make you happy to see me suffer?'

'Of course it doesn't. I know how you are suffering. I feel your pain.'

Della bit her lip, trying to hold back tears[32], the tears that she had held back all her life. 'Then why did you do this?'

Izod just raised a hand up. Out of the sea, two castles appeared, one blue, one red. Watery[33] figures[34] poured out of the Red Castle, marched[35] towards the Blue Castle and attacked it.

'I know the history of our lands,' Della admitted. 'I know it was wrong. But being queen is not easy. My mother has to do many things she doesn't want to do. And your people were dangerous. You had magic.'

'We all had magic, once.' Izod smiled. 'But they did not tell you that part of the story, did they? Once, we were all one, Blue and Red together.'

'What happened?' whispered[36] Della.

'We broke ourselves up[37] and killed our other half.'

Della shook her head. 'Why?'

'For the same reason that my people fear yours and your people hate mine. Unity[38] never lasts. It is nature's way to divide things. Animals kill each other, the sea destroys the land, and queens take countries.'

'Then why fight?' Della knew she was being selfish, but why couldn't the fairy leave her kingdom alone? Even if war had to happen, couldn't her people be happy?

'Della,' said Izod, putting a hand on the girl's shoulder. 'There is one last hope. A way for us to wake up and bring our peoples back together. But you will not like it. You won't be able to go back to your life in the sun. That castle has fallen down.'

Della looked into the fairy's eyes, deep pools of water. She had no reason to trust her. She was the monster that her parents had warned her about. And yet, her parents were also monsters themselves. She saw that now.

'Tell me.'

~

D ella woke up suddenly. No, she was not Della now. She was Izodella. She had her wings of water and she had her hair of fire.

Izodella floated out of bed and examined the dusty room she was in. Death and dirt had climbed into every part of the castle, and she knew immediately that her parents were gone. Many years had passed, and when she looked out of the window, she saw a dying land. The earth was Red, red with fire and blood, and she saw no joy[39] or bravery[40], only misery[41] and pain.

Without waiting, Izodella flew to the throne[42] room, and there, sitting on a throne twice as large as himself, was Sir Galen.

'Well, well, well. The Princess has finally decided to wake up.' He smiled. 'I think I preferred you asleep.'

The King's guards ran forward, but Izodella was faster than them. She dove[43] forward, pushing her hand into Galen's chest[44] and pulling out his heart. The King gave his last breath and fell onto the floor.

Then came the guards and the soldiers. They attacked her with weapons[45], but she killed them like flies[46], breaking through the castle doors and flying above it.

Below her, the people sweated[47] and bled[48] for their kingdom, and now they looked up at her in misery. The end had come, and they knew it.

Izodella raised her right hand.

Fire rained down. It ate up the Red Castle and ran across the land, burning through fields and forests. It climbed mountains and danced across rivers, and finally it reached the ruins of the Blue Castle, and ate it up like it had eaten up the Red.

Izodella raised her left hand.

Water rained down. It washed away the ashes[49] of the fire, pushed the bodies of the dead into the sea, and made the land clean.

Finally, the fire died and the rain stopped. The land slept. Izodella put down her hands and cried. She cried rivers and oceans, her tears pouring onto the dry earth. All around, silence and darkness[50] grew.

And then, where her tears had fallen, something rose[51] out of the dark, something this land had not seen for a very long time.

Green.

ONE-EYED, TWO-EYED, THREE-EYED

There was once an old woman who had three daughters. The eldest daughter had three eyes, so she was called Three-Eyed. The youngest daughter had one eye, so she was called One-Eyed. The middle daughter had two eyes, so she was called Two-Eyed. Three-Eyed was beautiful, and One-Eyed was very clever, but Two-Eyed was ugly and not very clever at all. She was, however, very hard-working[1]. Her sisters hated her because she had two eyes like normal people, and her mother hated her because she was not special like her sisters.

One day, the mother decided it was time for her daughters to get married.

'Three-Eyed will marry a rich businessman, since she is so beautiful. One-Eyed will marry an academic[2], since she is so clever.'

'And who will I marry, Mother?' asked Two-Eyed.

'Stupid girl!' she cried. 'You will not marry anyone. You will stay at home and look after your dear mother.'

So the old woman prepared her eldest and youngest daughters for marriage. She painted a second eye onto One-Eyed's face, so that it looked like she had two eyes. Then she took some horse hair and made a fringe[3] to put on Three-Eyed's head, so that her third eye could not be seen.

'There!' she said. 'Now, who wouldn't want to marry you?'

A few days later, a man came round looking for a wife.

'Come in, come in!' said the old woman. 'Perhaps you would like to marry my eldest daughter, who is very pretty?'

The man looked at Three-Eyed and said, 'Hmm, I think not.'

Ah, thought the old woman, *he is one of those men who prefer clever girls over pretty girls, because they worry that their wife will sleep with another man.*

'Well, perhaps you would prefer my youngest daughter? She is very clever.'

The man saw One-Eyed and said, 'She is not my type[4]. Where is the middle daughter?'

'Oh no, she is ugly and stupid. You do not want to marry her.'

Two-Eyed was hiding in the next room. She had seen the man through the window, and he was very handsome. She wouldn't let her mother prevent her from talking to him. She was allowed to say hello, wasn't she? So she walked into the room and smiled at him.

'Hello,' she said.

'Ah! *This* is the daughter I want to marry.'

'No, no!' said the mother. 'She does not want to get married.'

'But Mother, I—'

'Goodbye!'

And the mother pushed the man out of the door and shut it. Suddenly, the old woman, Three-Eyed and One-Eyed all turned on Two-Eyed.

'You think you're so clever, don't you?' said the mother. 'You cannot get married, you little brat[5]. I already told you.'

'Ugly girl!' said Three-Eyed.

'Stupid girl!' said One-Eyed.

Two-Eyed burst into tears and ran to her bed.

Meanwhile, the mother and the two favourite daughters thought about what to do. They needed to make sure no man wanted to marry Two-Eyed.

'Hrmm,' said One-Eyed, 'we could make her work very hard so that she is rough and ugly.'

'I have a better idea!' said the mother. 'We will make her work hard and give her no food. Every day, she'll work in the fields, and afterwards we'll give her just a third[6] of your food to eat. She'll turn thin and rough, and nobody will want to marry her!'

'Great idea, Mum!' said One-Eyed. 'I wish I had thought of that.'

So early the next day, Three-Eyed and One-Eyed pulled Two-Eyed out of bed, and told her she had work to do in the fields.

'What about breakfast?' she asked.

'No breakfast for you, lazy!' said Three-Eyed.

So the girl went to the field and started working. She watched the sun rise as she did so. It was a beautiful day, and she did not mind working hard, because her lunch would taste much better afterwards.

A few hours later, a goat came up to her[7].

'Meeeh! Good day, Two-Eyed.'

'How do you know my name?' the girl asked. 'And, oh! How can you talk?'

'I am no ordinary goat and you are no ordinary girl.'

'Oh, but I am ordinary. I am not beautiful like my older sister, and I am not clever like my younger sister. And I only have two eyes, just like you and everyone else.'

'Oh no, you are special. You just do not know it yet. But that is not important. I bet you are hungry.'

'Yes, I am quite hungry. But when I finish working, we will have lunch, I am sure.'

The goat shook his head[8]. 'They will only give you a third[9] of the food they eat. They made a plan last night. They will give you less and less food, so that you get thinner and thinner.'

'Oh!' said the girl.

'But do not worry. As I said, I am no ordinary goat. Say these magic words and I will help you: "Little goat, little goat, it's time to eat." When you are done, say, "Little goat, little goat, it's time to go." '

So the girl said, 'Little goat, little goat, it's time to eat.'

A pickle

Suddenly, the goat started changing. It grew long and square, and turned into a big white table. And on the table were all

kinds of food: bread, cheeses, jams, pickles, tomatoes, olives and so on. The girl was really quite hungry from the work, so she ate lots and lots of food, and when she was done, she said, 'Little goat, little goat, it's time to go.'

Green olives

The table turned back into a goat and smiled at her.

'See you tomorrow, Two-Eyed!' he said, and ran off into the distance.

When Two-Eyed finished her work and came home, lunch was already made. There was bread and cheese and olives, but the food did not look as nice as the food the goat had given her.

'I suppose you want to eat?' said the mother.

'No, thank you!' said Two-Eyed. 'I ate plenty of food yesterday.'

For several days, the mother and her two favourite daughters sent Two-Eyed into the fields to work, and she ate food from the goat's table, and none at home. This made the three horrible women think and think, and finally, the mother said, 'Enough! Tomorrow, One-Eyed, you will go with your sister into the field and find out what is happening. The brat[10] is probably stealing food from a farmer.'

So the next day, One-Eyed followed Two-Eyed into the fields.

'Why are you following me?' said Two-Eyed. 'Are you going to help me with the work?'

'Eugh, no way!' said One-Eyed. 'I'm just so *bored*, and I thought it might be fun to watch you work while I lie on the grass.'

So Two-Eyed worked in the field, and when she took a break, she sat down on the grass next to One-Eyed. When they were very young, they had liked each other. One-Eyed used to put her head in Two-Eyed's lap[11] and Two-Eyed would sing to her, and sometimes Two-Eyed missed those days.

'Oh, sister,' she said. 'Put your head in my lap and I'll sing you a song.'

One-Eyed scowled[12], but she did as Two-Eyed said.

'Sister, sister, are you asleep?

Or are you awake? Tell me, tell me.'

'I am awake,' said One-Eyed.

'Sister, sister, are you asleep?

Or are you awake? Tell me, tell me.'

'I am awake,' said One-Eyed.

Two-Eyed continued to sing, and her voice went quieter and quieter, until finally One-Eyed's eye closed and she fell asleep, and she did not answer the song. Then, Two-Eyed carefully got up, went and found the goat.

'Little goat, little goat, it's time to eat!'

The goat turned into a table, and the girl ate and ate, while her sister slept and slept. Then she said, 'Little goat, little goat, it's time to go!'

The goat went away, and Two-Eyed went and woke up her sister.

'Come on, sister! It is time to go home.'

'Oh!' said One-Eyed. 'Did I sleep for that long?'

That evening, their mother and Three-Eyed asked One-Eyed what she saw, but the girl told them she had fallen asleep.

'You stupid girl!' cried her mother.

'But I did see one thing!' One-Eyed said. 'When she woke me up, she had some cheese on her mouth.'

'Hmm.' The mother stroked[13] her chin. 'Tomorrow, Three-Eyed, you will go with her to the fields. And don't make a stupid mistake like your sister!'

So the next day, Three-Eyed joined Two-Eyed for her daily work. Of course, she was just as lazy as her sister, so she lay down in the grass and watched Two-Eyed smugly[14] until lunchtime.

Two-Eyed had never put Three-Eyed's head in her lap[15] and sang her songs, but she knew her older sister had been jealous[16] of One-Eyed. So Two-Eyed suggested they do it, too.

'Pah!' said Three-Eyed. 'I would never do something as silly as that.'

'Just for a moment, sister.'

'Fine. But only to show you how stupid it is.'

So Three-Eyed laid her head in Two-Eyed's lap and the girl sang to her.

'Sister, sister, are you asleep?

Or are you awake? Tell me, tell me.'

'I am awake,' said Three-Eyed.

'Sister, sister, are you asleep?

Or are you awake? Tell me, tell me.'

'I am awake,' said Three-Eyed.

Two-Eyed continued to sing, and her voice went quieter and quieter, until finally Three-Eyed's eyes closed, and she did not answer the song. Then, Two-Eyed carefully got up, went and found the goat.

But Three-Eyed was not asleep. Her two lower eyes were closed, but under her fringe[17], her third eye was open. Carefully, she moved aside[18] the fringe, and watched what Two-Eyed was doing.

'Little goat, little goat, it's time to eat!'

Three-Eyed saw the goat turn into a table, and she saw Two-Eyed eat her meal. Then the girl said, 'Little goat, little goat, it's time to go!'

That evening, Three-Eyed told her mother and sister everything that had happened. Her mother had never looked so happy before.

'She is a witch[19]!' said One-Eyed. 'We must tell the town and burn her.'

'No!' said the mother. 'I need someone to do the work here. I have a better idea. I think we will have goat for supper.'

'Yes,' said Three-Eyed, 'but what about the magic goat?'

'You stupid girl!' said the mother. 'We are going to *eat* the magic goat.'

'*Oh.*'

When Two-Eyed heard about this, she started crying, and she cried and cried all day. Then she fell asleep in her room, and had a strange dream.

In the dream, she was working in the fields, but the goat did not come to her. Instead, an old man visited.

'They are going to eat the goat,' he said.

'What can I do?' said Two-Eyed.

*Some animals have hard feet called hooves (singular **hoof**)*

Some animals have sharp things on their heads called horns

'After the meal is finished, take the goat's hooves and horns. Plant them behind the door. But make sure that nobody sees.'

The girl nodded[20], and woke up. It was late evening, and she could hear the loud laughter[21] of her mother and sisters from the kitchen.

'Two-Eyed!' screamed One-Eyed. 'Come and watch us eat!'

Reluctantly[22], Two-Eyed climbed out of bed and went into the kitchen. There, the family was eating a delicious goat curry. Two-Eyed felt sick, but she had to stay and watch them eat it all. Still, she did not cry.

After the meal was finished, her mother waved her hands at the pot and the plates and said, 'Clean up this mess, Two-Eyed.'

Two-Eyed waited for them to fall asleep, and then took the hooves and the horns from the bottom of the pot. She dug a hole[23] behind the door, working slowly and quietly, and planted the hooves and horns inside. Exhausted, she went to bed.

The next day, a beautiful apple tree had grown by the door. And it was no ordinary apple tree; the apples were made of gold!

'Daughters, daughters!' cried the mother. 'It is a miracle[24]!'

But when she tried to pick the apples, the branches of the tree moved away, and she could not reach them. As Three-Eyed was the tallest, she told her to pick them, but the branches moved away from her hands as well. So she got One-Eyed to stand on Three-Eyed's shoulders, but the same thing happened, and they both fell down onto the ground.

'It's not fair!' cried One-Eyed. 'Those are our golden apples!'

The mother looked at Two-Eyed and said, 'Don't even think about[25] picking any of these apples, or I will tell the town that you are a witch[26].'

But when they were not looking, Two-Eyed reached for the tree. The branches bent[27] down to her, and she easily picked one of the beautiful golden apples. She hid it in her dress and went back to work.

A few days later, the man from before came round again.

'I am still interested in your middle daughter,' he said. 'Are you sure she does not want to get married?'

'Yes, yes!' said the mother. 'But it does not matter. The horrible little girl ran away.'

Actually, Two-Eyed was under the bed, because her mother had told her to hide there.

'Oh, what a beautiful tree you have!' said the man. It reminded him of a dream he'd had... 'Those apples shine like gold. How did you grow such a tree?'

'We just looked after it well. Now, would you like to see my eldest daughter again? She really is very beautiful. Much prettier than my ugly middle daughter.'

The man thought for a moment, as he looked at the golden apples. Beauty was not the most important thing in a wife. But his father had been bothering him to get married, and if he found a beautiful wife, then people would think he was handsome, too. But it was such a shame that the middle daughter had disappeared!

If he married someone he did not love, she would need to be hard-working. He wasn't sure if One-Eyed or Three-Eyed had ever lifted a finger[28] in the house, so he decided to test them[29].

'Would your lovely daughters be able to pick me some apples?'

So the mother sent Three-Eyed and One-Eyed to the tree, but as much as they tried, they could not pick a single apple[30].

'How funny,' the man said. He did not sound happy.

Two-Eyed had been watching from under the bed and was growing more and more frustrated[31]. She had to do something, or she would be working for her mother and sisters for the rest of her life. She still had the golden apple *she* had picked, so she rolled[32] it out from under the bed.

'Oh!' said the man, picking it up. '*Here* is one of the apples, but where did it come from...?'

'I have no idea!' said the mother, taking the apple out of his hand. 'Three-Eyed must have picked it earlier.'

The man didn't listen, looking for where the apple had come from. And there, shining from under the bed, he saw two bright eyes.

'Ah,' he said, pulling Two-Eyed out, 'your daughter has not run away at all!'

Two-Eyed blushed[33], and could not look the man in the eyes. He raised a finger to her chin and turned her head up to face him.

He was gorgeous from this distance, and his eyes shone like the golden apples.

'Your mother says that you do not want to get married. Is this true?'

'No, no, not at all!' said Two-Eyed. 'I would love to marry you. That is, if you are—'

But before she could finish her sentence, the man kissed her.

'Yes,' he said softly.

Behind the two lovers, the rest of the family was going

mad. Three-Eyed was crying, the mother was pulling out her hair, and One-Eyed was still desperately[34] trying to pick an apple.

'You cannot leave!' said the mother, as Two-Eyed joined hands with the man and left the house.

But the couple didn't listen to her, and passed by the apple tree.

'I suppose you want me to pick you an apple?' said Two-Eyed. 'To prove I am a hard-working girl.'

'Oh no, not at all,' he said. 'That's what my father's always saying, that I must find a wife who will work hard in the midday sun. But I don't think that's important. I had a strange dream a few nights ago. An old man came and told me that I must marry the girl whose eyes shine like gold, and I believe I have found her.'

Two-Eyed was so overcome with feelings[35] that she did not know what to say. Instead, she just kissed him.

So they went and got married, and lived happily ever after[36]. And the mother and her two favourite daughters never, ever in their long lives, could pick an apple from the tree.

THE BOY WHO KNEW NO FEAR

Once, there was a father with two sons. He loved one and hated the other. The older son, Hugh, was smart, sensible and talented, while the younger son, Anders, was a good-for-nothing[1]. Whenever the father needed something, Hugh was always quick to help him, while Anders sat around and did nothing.

But when he asked Hugh to go somewhere late at night, the boy turned white and cried, 'Oh no, Father, I can't go out in the night! It makes me shudder[2] so.' And when his father told ghost stories by the fire, Hugh often said, 'Oh, it makes me shudder!'

Anders could not understand what his brother was talking about. There was nothing strange about the night. It was a lovely time, when the moon shone and the town was quiet. And he could not understand why Hugh didn't like Father's ghost stories, either, since he always told them so well.

'He is always saying, "It makes me shudder, it makes me shudder!" It does not make *me* shudder, although I don't know what that means.'

One day, the father said to Anders, 'Alright, boy. You are stupid, but you have grown tall and strong. You can make a living[3], but you'll need to learn something first. Your brother studied woodwork[4], which will be too hard for you, but I'm sure we can find something. What do you think?'

'Actually, Father,' he said, 'I know exactly what I want to learn. I want to learn how to *shudder*. I simply don't understand[5] it.'

Hugh, who was listening through the door, hit his head and said, 'God, if only I had a donkey for a brother. Then he'd at least know *something*.'

'You want to learn how to *shudder*?' said Anders' father. 'I can teach you how to shudder right now, you stupid boy. Just get my belt.'

'Oh, you really will?' said Anders excitedly. 'Then please!'

He ran to get his father's belt, but his father shouted, 'Stop! It was a joke, you idiot[6].' He wanted to shut Anders up[7], but he wanted him to leave his home more. Perhaps if he helped him learn how to shudder, the boy would leave forever.

A few days later, there was the perfect opportunity, when a priest came to visit the house. The father invited him for a cup of tea and told him all about his son.

Hearing this, the priest smiled and said, 'Ah, you truly[8]

have a special child. God sends us these children to test[9] us, and I am confident I can help him. Let him live with me, and I will teach him how to shudder.

The father said yes, and sent Anders to live with the priest.

A man ringing a bell

The priest lived in a house next to the church, and taught Anders about bell ringing. There was a great bell in the tower, and every day, Anders climbed up to ring it. After a few days of this, the priest decided it was time Anders learned how to shudder. He woke him up in the middle of the night and told him to go ring the bell. While Anders was getting ready, the priest sneaked[10] up there before him.

The boy was just about to ring the bell when he heard a noise behind him. He turned around and saw a man dressed in white bedsheets[11], standing at the top of the stairs.

'Who's that?' said Anders.

But the man in white did not reply. He simply stood there[12], and made strange noises.

'Answer me,' said Anders, 'or leave. You have no business here.'

The 'ghost' made louder noises, and the boy didn't understand what this strange man was doing.

'Look, I have a bell to ring and I don't want to stay up here all night. Say something, man, or I'll throw you down the stairs!'

He doesn't really mean that, thought the priest. *He's very good at hiding his fear, but I can see that his fear is growing.*

But Anders was not afraid, just annoyed. Why would he be scared of a man wearing bedsheets? The man continued to make strange noises, and Anders had had enough. So he ran and pushed him down the stairs.

The 'ghost' screamed and fell ten steps backwards.

'That'll teach you[13] to wear strange clothes and bother strangers in the night,' he said.

Then he rang the bell, walked past the 'ghost', and went to bed.

The priest's wife, meanwhile, was waiting for her husband to come back. He was gone for a very long time, and she started to worry, so she went and woke Anders.

'What is it now?!' he said. 'Does "shuddering" mean to be constantly[14] woken up in the night?'

'Have you seen my husband? He went up to the tower before you.'

'Funny. No, I didn't see him. There was just a strange man dressed in white, making odd[15] noises, and since he refused to answer my questions, I pushed him down the stairs.'

Horrified[16], the wife ran up to the tower and found her husband crying in pain. He had broken his leg.

The next day, she went straight to Anders' father and shouted at him.

'Your boy has caused us great problems[17]! He threw my husband down the stairs and broke his leg. We don't want him anymore.'

The father pulled Anders out of the house by his ear and said, 'What did you do, you stupid boy?!'

'Father,' said Anders, 'I did nothing wrong. That man followed me into the tower at night, dressed in white bedsheets, and stood there making strange noises. He wouldn't answer my questions, so I pushed him down the stairs. Aren't you proud of me?'

His father turned completely white.

'Ah yes, he looked a bit like that!'

'I have nothing to say to you, boy. Leave, and never come back.'

'I agree, Father. I think I can learn to shudder by myself.'

The father said, 'Wait! I will not let you walk out to a cold death just like that. Take this money, but do not tell anyone who your father is.'

Anders smiled. 'Thanks, Dad!'

Anders walked out of town and through a forest, saying the whole time, 'If only I could shudder!'

A few hours later, he walked past a tree where seven men were hanged. Anders looked up at the tree and scratched[18] his head. What were they doing up there? It looked very uncomfortable.

There was another traveller going along that road at the same time, a conman[19]. He saw Anders looking up at the tree and thought, *That boy looks particularly stupid, and it's so easy to con stupid boys. I think I'll have some fun with him.*

He walked up to Anders and said, 'Hello, traveller! Where are you going?'

Hanging is an old way to kill people. People were hanged on ropes like this.

'I'm going to learn how to shudder,' said Anders smugly[20]. It was such an exciting thing to learn, since he had no idea what it was.

The conman laughed. This was going to be *very* easy.

'Well, then you've found the right man! I can teach you how to shudder, and I'll do it for free.'

'Oh no, sir!' said Anders. 'You can't give that to me for free. No, if you teach me, I'll give you *all* my money.'

The conman licked his lips[21]. 'Alright, then! Take a look up at that tree there.' He pointed at the place where the seven men were hanged. 'Those seven men wanted to marry the baker's daughter, and the baker wanted to make sure they were suitable for her. So he told them that the man who can fly will take his daughter as a wife, and there they are, learning how to fly.'

'Wow!' said Anders. 'I want to join them.'

He started climbing the tree, but the conman grabbed his arm.

'Not quite yet! You wouldn't want to learn how to fly before you've learned how to shudder, would you?'

Anders thought for a moment. 'I suppose not. Can I do both at once?'

'Oh, by the time I've taught you you'll be flying, shuddering and dancing all at once! Sit by the tree and wait for the night, and *don't* fall asleep. By the morning, you will have learned how to shudder.'

'Brilliant!' said Anders.

'Sweet dreams!' said the conman. 'I'll see you tomorrow.'

'But you said not to sleep!' cried Anders as the man left.

Honestly, some people were terrible at giving instructions. But he did as the man said and sat by the tree.

As it got dark, it also got cold, so Anders made a fire. Then a sharp wind blew, and the hanged men swayed[22] in the wind.

Of course, the men were *not* learning to fly, and the conman thought that Anders would realise this. Then he would find the swaying men very frightening. But he had underestimated just how stupid Anders really was[23].

'You must be cold up there!' he called.

The men did not answer.

'Hello? How is it going? Getting close to flying?'

Again, the men did not answer. How rude! But they really did look cold, so Anders decided to help them. He climbed up the tree and cut them down. They fell onto the ground with a PLOP and he put them by the fire to warm up. But they didn't just warm up—their clothes caught on fire, and the men did nothing to stop it!

'Wow, you really are quite stupid!' said Anders. 'Aren't you going to move away? Or is this part of learning how to fly?'

The dead men did not reply, and their clothes continued to burn. This made Anders quite angry.

'No good teacher would make you burn your own clothes like that! I can't stand watching you waste the fabric[24]. Your mothers must have sewn[25] for hours to make those!'

So Anders hanged them back on the tree, and then went and slept by the fire. The man had said he shouldn't sleep, but he couldn't see how he was going to learn to shudder from these foolish[26] men.

The next day, the conman found him in the morning light.

'Well, did you learn how to shudder?'

'No!' said Anders, leaping to his feet[27]. 'Those men were so stupid! They wouldn't answer my questions, and then they let their clothes burn, even though their mothers had worked hard to make them. How could I learn to shudder from such foolish, selfish people?'

The conman couldn't believe his ears. In fact, he was so surprised that he shuddered. But before he could ask for his payment[28], the boy was already leaving.

'Wait!' he called. 'What about my money?'

'I learned nothing from you!' shouted Anders.

So the boy continued out of the forest and passed through a village, always saying, 'If only I could shudder!'

A man from the village saw him and thought, *That boy looks lost. I should help him.*

He stopped him and asked, 'What are you called, boy?'

Anders thought for a moment. 'Well, my father always calls me "stupid".'

'And where are you from?'

'A house. Isn't everyone?'

The villager sighed[29]. This wasn't going to be easy.

'Who is your father?'

Anders' face suddenly turned serious. 'I cannot tell you.'

'And what is it you were saying to yourself, just now?'

'I said, "If only I could shudder!" You see, I want to learn to shudder.'

The man frowned[30]. 'Why would you want to learn that? Well, I know a way you can learn, but it won't be pleasant.'

'Oh, please, sir! I'll do *anything* to learn how to shudder. How much should I pay you?'

The man licked his lips[31]. He'd wanted to help the boy, but it appeared that this boy was beyond help[32]. And didn't he deserve a financial reward for being such a good person and helping people like this?

'I'll accept whatever money you have to offer. Uh, maybe more than that. Yes, that's perfect.'

Anders gave him the money and he continued.

'Well then, you've probably heard of the King, but many don't know that he lived in a different castle before. Now it is empty, and only ghosts and monsters live there. The King is looking for a man brave enough to stay in the castle for three nights. The man who does so will be given his daughter's hand in marriage[33], and she is the most beautiful woman to ever exist.'

He didn't mention her personality[34]. The stay in the haunted[35] castle was to show the Princess's husband could handle her cruel ways. She was famous for playing tricks[36] on people.

'I get to learn how to shudder *and* marry a princess? Awesome!'

'There is more. There are also fantastic treasures[37] in the castle. If you succeed, you will gain the treasures and the girl, and you will live happily for the rest of your life.'

'How wonderful!' said Anders. He couldn't understand why nobody had stayed in the castle already. Ghosts and monsters were a bit odd[38], but they were quite fun, too.

The villager saw that Anders didn't understand the danger and suddenly felt bad. He couldn't let the boy just walk into his death.

'Many men have gone into the castle, but none have left,' he said.

Hmm, thought Anders. *Perhaps it is simply a very comfortable castle and they saw no reason to leave.*

So Anders went and told the King he would stay in the castle.

'You're very brave, my boy,' said the King. 'You may take three things with you into the castle.'

'Wow, this just gets easier and easier! In that case... I would like a fire, a knife and a lathe[39].'

He hated sleeping in the cold, so a fire was essential. Knives were always useful, too. And he'd seen his brother playing with his lathe, when he did woodwork[40]. Anders had always wanted to try it, but his brother never let him.

An axe (pronunciation **AKS**). *People use axes to cut wood.*

'A lathe? Are you sure? Don't you want something more useful? Maybe an axe? What can a lathe do?'

'A lathe can do lots of things!' said Anders. 'At least, my brother does lots with it.'

'Fine, fine. But do be careful, my boy.'

'It's just a haunted[41] castle,' said Anders. 'What could go wrong?'

So Anders went to the castle, which was lying in ruins[42]. Anders had never seen ruins before, so he thought, *Wow, what a strange architectural decision. It looks interesting, but it's so cold with all those holes in the ceiling!*

He found a nice room with a chair in it, so he made a fire and sat down by the lathe.

'If only I could shudder!' he said. 'Somehow, I don't think I'm going to learn it here.'

Just then, he heard a cry from a dark corner.

'Ow, meow! It is so cold!'

'If you are cold, come and sit by the fire, silly!'

Two great black cats jumped out of the darkness[43] and sat beside him. Their eyes shone bright red. They sat by the fire, warming themselves, before saying, 'Ow, meow! Shall we play a game of cards?'

Anders didn't like the look of these cats. Black cats knew magic, his mother always told him. So he said, 'Yes, let's. But first, I wonder, do black cats have black paws? Or do you have pink paws like other cats?'

'Ow, meow! Don't worry about our paws, boy.' They suddenly seemed very shy, and moved back into the darkness[44].

Anders raised an eyebrow[45]. 'Well, if you won't show me your paws, then I won't play your games.'

So the cats raised their paws up to show that they were pink, and they had *very* sharp claws.

A paw (animal hand) with long claws (they can hurt you!)

'Oh, what long claws you have! Let me cut them for you. I have a knife.'

'No!' said the cats, taking their paws away. 'We need them to hold onto the cards.'

Anders shook his head. 'But you'll just scratch[46] them! I can't play cards if they're all covered in scratches. Please, let me cut your claws.'

'Fine,' said the cats.

They came close, and Anders saw his opportunity. He grabbed the cats by the throat and held the knife up at them. 'I know what you want, you monsters! You want to claw my eyes out[47], or use magic on me! Well no, thank you!'

And with that, he threw the cats out of the window. They meowed and screamed as they fell into the water below. But before Anders could sit down again, hundreds of black cats and black dogs leapt[48] out of the darkness.

Their eyes all shone bright red, and they shouted and bit at him, and tried to put out the fire.

'Get back, you beasts[49]!' he shouted.

He waved his knife around, and some of the animals cried and ran away. Others stayed and fought, and those ones he grabbed by the ears and threw them out the window. But the animals kept coming and coming, filling the room, pushing him to the floor. He was losing hope, but at the stroke of midnight[50], all the creatures suddenly disappeared.

When Anders sat down again, he felt very tired. He turned around and saw a bed in the corner.

'Perfect!' he said, and climbed into the bed.

But as he fell asleep, the bed started moving. He opened his eyes, and saw that the bed was crawling[51] around the room like a bug.

'Wonderful,' he said. 'That will help me fall asleep. But go a bit faster, would you?'

So the bed ran and ran, moving around the castle like a horse, and Anders made himself very comfortable. The bed then flipped over[52], so that it was lying on top of him.

'That's no fun,' he said. 'I can't sleep like that.' He pushed the bed off him and went to sleep by the fire.

In the morning, the King came and saw him lying still on the floor.

'Oh no, the poor boy! The ghosts and monsters killed him.'

'What are you talking about?' said Anders, sitting up[53].

'You're alive! What happened?'

'Good morning to you, too! Many things happened last night, but the important thing is, I did *not* learn how to shudder. Still, it was a very lively evening anyway.'

'You mean, you were not afraid?'

'Of course not! I slept very well.'

So the next night Anders went back into the haunted castle and said again, 'If only I could shudder!'

This time, there were no cats or dogs, but a few hours later, he heard a loud scream, and something fell from the chimney[54]. It was a man, but only the top half of him. He was missing his legs and feet, and blood was pouring out[55] of him.

'Hello!' cried Anders. 'That must be quite uncomfortable. Where's the rest of your body?'

Then there was another scream, and the other half of the man fell down.

'Let me make a fire for you,' he said, thinking that the man might be cold.

When he turned around, the two halves had joined back together, and the man was sitting on the chair with an evil[56] smile on his face.

'Excuse me, that chair is mine.'

Anders pushed him onto the floor.

The man jumped to his feet. 'We'll see whose chair it is! Let us play a game.'

He clapped his hands, and some leg bones fell from the chimney, with human feet on the ends.

'Ooh, we're going to go bowling!' said Anders. 'I love

this game.' He placed the leg bones in a triangle and then looked around. 'But uh, where is the ball?'

*Bowling (pronunciation **BO-ling**)*

The evil man rolled his eyes[57] and clapped his hands again. This time, some skulls fell down.

'These are terrible balls! They're not round at all.'

'They'll be more than good enough—'

'No!' said Anders. 'If we're going to play, we're going to do it right.'

So he took the skulls and put them on the lathe, working them until they were round.

*A triangle (pronunciation **TRAI-an-gul**)*

'There! Now they'll roll[58] perfectly.'

A skull

They went bowling, and Anders did quite badly, but he had a lot of fun. The man wanted to scare[59] him, but Anders didn't understand why the man kept saying, 'Boo!' Once more, at the stroke of midnight[60], everything disappeared: the man, the skulls and the leg bones.

'Oh no! I did not get to say goodbye.'

With nothing else to do, Anders lay down and went to sleep.

The next morning, the King came and spoke to him again.

'How was it this time?'

'Quite fun! We went bowling, although my friend did not say goodbye.'

'But you did not learn how to shudder?'

'No! I'm starting to think I'll *never* learn…'

On the third night, Anders sat sadly[61] on his chair and said, 'If only I could shudder!'

A few hours later, six tall men with white faces entered the room with a coffin[62], which they placed on the ground before Anders.

Hmm, thought Anders. *Why would they be bringing me a coffin?*

Then he remembered that his cousin had died recently. Perhaps they were bringing him his body so he could say goodbye?

The six men opened the coffin, but the man inside was too big to be Anders' cousin. Still, the boy was convinced[63] that it was him, and said, 'Cousin! You look so cold. Let me warm you up.'

So he warmed his hand on the fire and held it to the man's face. But the body stayed cold. Anders carried him out of the coffin and put him by the fire, but this didn't help either. Finally, Anders put him in the bed and wrapped him in the bedsheets.

The body warmed up and started to move.

'See, cousin? You must feel much better, now that you are warm. I never understood why dead people have to sleep in coffins, anyway. It must be so cold under the ground.'

The dead man sat up and cried, 'Foolish[64] boy! Now I will eat you!'

'What?!' said Anders. 'That's how you thank me, by trying to eat me? You always were my least favourite cousin. Back to the coffin!'

He picked up his 'cousin', threw him back into the coffin and shut it. The six white men came back, rolled their eyes[65] at Anders, and took the coffin away.

'Don't you want to stay for a round of bowling[66]? Ugh, fine. I don't think I will *ever* learn to shudder!'

'I can help you with that…'

Anders turned around and saw an old man with a long white beard, standing in the darkness.

'You will shudder the whole time while I strangle[67] you!'

'Strangle me? That doesn't sound very fun!'

'I don't care! I'm going to kill you!'

The man jumped at Anders, but the boy pushed him to the ground.

'I don't think so. You're not very strong.'

'Oh, I might not *look* strong, but I am,' said the old man, standing up. 'Fine then, let's have a little competition. Follow me…'

The man guided Anders through many dark passages[68]. Finally, they arrived in a room with two big stones and an axe.

'It's very simple. We will each try to break the stone in two to see who is stronger.'

The old man grabbed the axe and held it up. His beard dangled[69] as he moved. He swung[70] the axe, breaking the stone in two with it.

Anders was worried. He didn't think he was strong enough to break his stone, and he really didn't want to be strangled. But he wasn't scared. He had a plan.

'Pah! I can do better than that.'

He took the axe and held it above the second stone. The old man stood and watched. Anders waited and waited, holding the axe but not moving. The old man moved closer and closer, his beard dangling in front of him. When he was close enough, Anders dropped the axe, grabbed the man's beard, and pulled it between the two broken pieces of stone. Then he pushed the stone together, trapping his beard inside[71].

'Hey, hey!' cried the old man. 'I can't move! That's not fair!'

'Now I have you,' said Anders. 'You were going to strangle me, you nasty old thing!'

Then he took a piece of stone and beat[72] the old man with it.

'Please stop!' he cried. 'I'm sorry I threatened[73] to strangle you! I'll show you where the treasures are hidden!'

Anders' arm got tired, so he stopped. He had completely forgotten about the treasures and the Princess, but he supposed that it would be nice to have them. Even if he didn't learn to shudder here, he would have something.

'Fine, then.'

He released[74] the old man, who showed him a hidden door in the wall. It led to a room with three huge chests[75] full of treasure.

'One of these chests is for the poor, one is for the King, and the other is yours.'

'Oh, so the monsters like giving to the poor, do they?'

But just at that moment, it turned midnight, and the old man disappeared. All the candles in the room went out, leaving Anders in the darkness. He carefully found his way back to the fire and slept there.

The next morning, the King came and said, 'Surely now you have learnt[76] what shuddering is?'

'No, I have not. My dead cousin visited, and then a bearded man[77] came and showed me where the treasure is, but *nobody* taught me to shudder.'

The King gasped[78]. 'Then you have succeeded, and you can marry my daughter!'

'Yes, yes, hooray[79] for Anders, hooray for the poor. But I don't care about all that! I still don't know how to shudder!'

The King made him show him to the treasures. They carried out the three chests, gave one to the poor, one to the King, and one to Anders. Then they held a great wedding, and Anders finally met his bride.

Just as the people had said, she was a cruel, unusual woman. She played all kinds of tricks[80] on Anders, so he started playing tricks on her, too, which she loved. They had lots of fun together, and she never called him stupid, so he fell in love with her.

But still, Anders could not be fully happy. Every night, when he went to bed, he sighed[81] and said, 'If only I could shudder!'

Finally, this was too much for his wife. 'Fine then, I will really show him how to shudder!'

She woke up early in the morning and went out to the river. She filled a bucket with cold water and fish and carried it inside. Then she poured the bucket right over Anders' head!

Anders sat up and cried, 'Oh, what makes me shudder so much? What makes me shudder so, my wife? Ah! Finally I know how to shudder!'

And they lived happily ever after[82].

CINDERELLA

Once, there was a poor girl called Cinderella. Her mother had died when she was young, and her father married another woman. Cinderella's stepmother[1] was a horrible person, and had two of her own daughters: Freta and Greta.

Freta and Greta treated Cinderella like dirt[2]. They made her do all the cooking, cleaning and sewing, and when their father tried to suggest that *they* do some work, their mother always said, 'Don't be so cruel!' So Cinderella lived a sad life, doing all the work in the house, wearing ugly, torn clothes and sleeping in the dust and ashes[3] on the floor.

The only nice thing in Cinderella's life was the hazel tree in the garden. She had planted it over her mother's grave[4] when she died, and it grew big and strong. Every night, Cinderella sat by the tree and cried. Sometimes, when she sat against the tree, she felt like her mother was holding her. She was great friends with two little birds who lived in the tree, and when her stepsisters[5] weren't looking, she liked to play with them and sing songs.

One day, while Cinderella was cleaning the kitchen under the eyes of her stepsisters, her stepmother came in to make an announcement.

Hazel trees make hazelnuts, that look like this.

'The King has announced a ball[6] and all are invited,' she said, holding out a letter.

Freta and Greta laughed and clapped, until their mother held out her hand to silence them.

'It will be three days long—'

More cries of happiness.

'—and there, the Prince will choose his new wife.'

The two sisters gasped[7], already dreaming about dancing with the handsome prince and becoming his wife.

Cinderella had never been to a ball before, but she had always wanted to go to one. And this was in the palace! Oh, what wonderful people would be there, what beautiful clothes, what delicious food... She didn't care much about the Prince, because she had never met him, but she wanted very much to go to the ball.

Over the next few days, the family started getting ready. Greta and Freta went into town with their mother to buy dresses. Every day, they asked Cinderella to make new bows, try out new kinds of hair and change their dresses, but the next day they always changed their mind and asked her to do something else.

In a quiet moment, Cinderella went to her father and asked him if she could go to the ball. He was trying to avoid the whole situation, but when she asked, he smiled.

'I don't see why not!'

*A bow (pronunciation **BO**)*

Cinderella understood that she could go, and over the next few days she did her best to make some nice clothes for herself, hiding her work from her stepsisters[8].

But on the day of the ball, when Cinderella put on her dress and said she was ready to go, Freta and Greta simply laughed in her face.

'You want to go to the King's ball in *that*?! That dress looks like it was made by rats! It's not even good enough to wear for a walk down the road.'

'But Father said—'

'Cinderella!' cried her stepmother[9]. 'Do you really think we would allow you to go to the ball and embarrass[10] us? If you were invited, I would have told you.'

'Don't worry, Cindy!' said Freta. 'You'll have something to do.'

'Here you go!' said Greta, giving her a pot filled with lentils. 'While we're gone, pick out the bad lentils from the good ones.'

'If there's even *one* bad lentil in there when we come back, you'll have to start again!'

Different types of lentils

Holding back tears[11], Cinderella watched her family climb into their carriage[12] and ride off to the palace.

Oh, how awful she felt! She poured all the lentils out on the floor, but it was clear that the work would take at least until midnight, and she didn't have the energy to do it.

She ran outside and threw herself onto the ground next to her mother's tree, crying into the earth.

A minute later, she heard a bird singing by her ear, and looked up to see her two bird friends.

'What's wrong, Cinderella?' said one of them.

'You can talk?'

'Of course, of course. What's wrong, Cinderella?'

'Oh, it's only that… I was being stupid, really. I thought I could go to the King's ball, but of course I can't. I have to pick out lentils in the dust while my sisters dance with wonderful people.'

'Show us these lentils, show us.'

So Cinderella took the birds inside and showed them the pile of lentils.

'We can help, we can help! We will eat the bad ones and leave the good ones.'

'Oh, thank you. But I still cannot go to the ball!'

'Cinderella, Cinderella. Go out to the tree and shake it.'

The birds started working, and Cinderella walked sadly to the tree. She did not know why they were asking her to shake the tree, but she did as she was told.

Out of the tree fell a large hazelnut. She opened the hazelnut, but inside there was not a nut[13], but a beautiful green gown[14]! It was as beautiful as a fresh flower in spring.

Cinderella carefully shook the tree again, and another nut fell. This time, there was not a dress inside, but a pair of gorgeous green shoes!

Her heart beating fast, she tried on the dress and shoes, and they fit her perfectly.

'Oh, Mother, thank you! But how can I go to the ball without a carriage[15]?'

She shook the tree once more, and another nut fell. When she opened this one, a beautiful carriage with two horses and a servant[16] jumped out.

'Wow!' she said. 'I must go and get ready!'

Cinderella ran inside, washed herself, combed her hair and put on the gown. She hardly recognised herself without the usual dirt and torn clothes. She was beautiful.

The birds had finished with the lentils, and they flew around her happily, singing, 'To the ball, to the ball! But be careful, my dear. You must return before midnight, or all will be lost.'

Cinderella climbed into the carriage and rode to the ball. She could hardly believe it was happening, and when she arrived at the palace, she felt like she was dreaming.

Everything was just as she had imagined it. The

building was made of beautiful white
stone, with marble stairs going to the
entrance, and inside it was filled with
magnificent coloured lights, flowers
from all around the world, and the
most elegant[17] guests with the most
wonderful dresses.

Marble, a type of stone

Cinderella felt uncomfortable. She didn't belong here.
Her dress was so simple compared to everyone else, and
she didn't know how to dance.

For a while, she just watched the dances, but not long
after, a man came and spoke to her.

'May I dance with you?'

He was the most handsome man she had ever met,
with hair as black as the night and eyes that shone like
stars.

'Yes, of course,' she said, taking his hand.

As the two danced, she felt all eyes turn to her. He was
handsome, but why was everyone looking at him? Whis-
pers[18] went around the room, and as they danced she
heard bits of conversation: '...beautiful girl...' '...who is
she?...' '...and with the Prince!'

Cinderella went as red as a tomato. She was dancing
with the Prince himself!

The Prince smiled at her, saying, 'You dance well for
someone who's never done it before.'

'How did you know?'

'It's obvious, but don't worry. I like it.'

They continued to dance, and Cinderella saw her

sisters standing in the corner. Freta and Greta were making faces like frogs.

Cinderella smiled and let herself enjoy the dance. By the time the song ended, she felt free, until she heard the clock strike eleven[19].

Suddenly, she remembered what the birds had said: return before midnight or all will be lost.

'I must go,' said Cinderella, moving out of the Prince's hands.

'Wait! Please stay for another dance.'

'Perhaps tomorrow night,' she said, before hurrying out the door.

She felt the Prince's stare[20] on her back as she went. She ran down the marble stairs into her carriage and rode home.

Her heart beat madly the whole way. Never in her life had she experienced such happiness. She wondered if her sisters had seen her, and hoped that they were too stupid to realise it was her.

When she arrived home, she quickly hid the dress and shoes in the tree in the garden, changed into her normal clothes, messed up[21] her hair and put dust and dirt on her face.

When the others returned a few hours later, Cinderella heard Freta say, 'I hope Cinderella hasn't fallen asleep while working on those lentils!'

'Forget the lentils,' said Greta. 'Who was that strange girl?'

Cinderella's family came in to see her, and she put on a

miserable face, so that they thought she had spent the whole evening picking out lentils on the floor.

'Done already?' said Freta. 'We'll give you something more challenging tomorrow night.'

'Come on, Sister,' said Greta. 'Let's go to bed.'

Cinderella smiled and said, 'Good night!'

Her stepmother stared at her. 'Your hair looks different.'

This woman has her hair tied up in a ponytail.

'Oh?' said Cinderella, touching it. 'I tied it up while I worked.'

'Hrmm. Do not get any strange ideas in your head about going to the ball tomorrow night or the night after that. You will stay here and work, understand?'

'Yes, Stepmother.'

'That's "Mother", you little...!' She raised her hand to hit Cinderella, who covered her head with her hands and shut her eyes. But her stepmother took a deep breath and did not hit her. 'Good night, Cinderella.'

There was no doubt about it. She knew that something strange was going on.

Cinderella hardly slept that night, as she couldn't stop thinking about the ball. Oh, how handsome the Prince had been!

The next day, her sisters gave her double the chores[22] to work on, but she worked with great energy, cleaning everything in no time.

'Why are you smiling so much, Cinderella?' said Greta. 'You're not going to the ball, you know!'

'Oh, I know! I just had a lovely dream.'

'Well, dream on!' said Freta.

Part of Cinderella's happiness came from hearing her sisters' conversation. Clearly, *everyone* had been talking about her dance with the Prince, and it was great to hear how bothered they were by it. If only they knew!

That night, Freta and Greta dropped a huge bag of seeds[23] into Cinderella's hands. Then, deciding that was too nice, they knocked it on the floor.

'Pick out the good seeds, lazy,' said Freta.

'And if we find even *one* bad one in there—'

'—you'll make me start again?'

Greta made a face. 'Yeah. Now shut your mouth and get to work!'

When the rest of the family had left, Cinderella's bird friends came in through the window.

'Oh, I know it is a lot to ask, but... would you help me again tonight?'

'Of course, Cinderella, of course!' sang the birds. 'Go and shake the tree, shake shake shake.'

So Cinderella ran out to the garden and shook the hazel tree once more. She was worried that the beautiful gifts might not fall down, but luckily, they did.

This time, she had a gorgeous blue gown, blue as the sea, with a pair of long gloves and dancing shoes. The shoes had a small heel, but after trying them on,

Cinderella found she could walk just fine, and she felt beautiful in them.

'Goodbye, little birds!' she said, running out to the carriage, 'and thank you once more!'

'Remember, remember, return before midnight!'

This time, when Cinderella arrived everyone was waiting for her. There were gasps[24] as she entered the room, as they clearly had not been expecting her to be even more beautiful than the night before. Several men immediately came up to ask for a dance, but she refused them all, as there was only one she was interested in.

'I must admit,' said the Prince as they started to dance, 'I was worried you wouldn't return after your quick exit last night.'

'I apologise for my rudeness[25].'

'Are you going to tell me why you left? I had to wonder...'

'Don't worry, it was not because of you. I had... to do something.'

'Well, you are just as mysterious[26] as you are beautiful. Will you at least tell me where you are from?'

'I come from not far from here.'

'And yet I have never heard of you until this moment! Won't you at least tell me your name?'

'I am Bridget.'

That was Cinderella's true name, that her mother had chosen before she died. She was sure that her sisters would not remember it, having used her other name for so long.

'A beautiful name.'

This time, Cinderella danced until past eleven, but as the time moved nearer to midnight, she kept looking at the clock.

'You have things to do tonight as well?'

'Yes, I am afraid, my Prince.'

'Well, will I at least see you again tomorrow night?'

'Absolutely.'

'Then I suppose I can let you go,' he said, smiling.

So Cinderella left once more, running down the steps and into the carriage before anyone else could talk to her.

Once again, after arriving home she hid the dress and shoes, made herself dirty and acted as if she had been working all evening. She made sure to mess up[27] her hair just the way it had been before.

'Oh, I'll kill that girl!' said Greta, as they walked through the door.

'Some were saying she is a foreign princess,' said Freta. 'Pah! I think she looked *horrible* in that dress.'

'Girls, go to bed,' said their mother. 'No talking through the night, understood?'

'Yes, mother!' they cried.

They stuck their heads into the room[28] where Cinderella was.

'We're going to give you *even more* work tomorrow, Cindy!'

Then they climbed up the stairs, laughing and chatting about the handsome men they had met.

Cinderella was ready to sleep as well, but once again her stepmother came in to see her.

'Cinderella, dear child.'

Cinderella felt an icy cold pass through her body. Her stepmother only called her 'dear child' when she wanted something.

'Yes, Mother?'

'Remind me what name you had previously.'

Cinderella quickly said, 'Britney.' She should have chosen something much more different to her real name, but it just came out of her mouth.

'Oh?' said her stepmother. 'I was sure you were called Bridget.'

'To be honest, Mother, I am so used to my new name that I can hardly remember my old one!'

'Hmm,' said her stepmother. 'Well, you have worked well again tonight. Do not disappoint me tomorrow.'

Cinderella slept badly that night. She had nightmares of her stepmother. She dreamt that she travelled to the ball for the final night, but as she danced, her stepmother came and took off her dress, showing her awful rags[29] underneath.

'See? She is only a common[30] servant[31] girl!'

Cinderella woke up feeling sick.

That day, her sisters gave her plenty of chores, just like they had said. She had to water the flowers, cut the grass and feed all the animals, as well as her usual cleaning. But as she worked, she heard her sisters talking.

'Oh, it is so sad that we only have one more night! I am not sure we have had a real chance yet…'

'Don't worry, tonight is the night! We'll dance with *him* tonight, and it doesn't matter what that ugly girl does. We're going to get married!'

'Not "we", stupid! We can't share a prince! He's going to be *mine*.'

'No! He'll be mine!'

They started fighting[32], but their words troubled Cinderella. She had enjoyed the ball so much that she had hardly thought about the future. As lovely as the Prince was, she would never be with him forever, because at midnight the magic would end and all her lovely clothes would disappear. She would be a dirty, common[33] servant girl, and he would be the handsome Prince.

Still, that night she couldn't stop herself from getting excited. It was only three nights, but they would be the most wonderful three nights of her life, and she did not intend to waste this one with worries of the future.

This time, her sisters gave her three giant bags of peas to sort through.

'You'll be working all night with these!' said the girls as they went out the door. 'If you don't see us again, it's because we're getting married to the Prince!'

Cinderella waved goodbye, making herself not smile. Then, after she was sure they were gone, she let the birds in.

'I feel so bad giving you so much work…'

'Of course not, of course not! It's the last night, the last night. Go and enjoy yourself!'

So while the birds worked, she went and shook the tree. Tonight, the dress was the most beautiful one yet. It was a gorgeous long silver gown, covered in shining stones, with a pair of high heels.

'I don't know if I'll be able to walk in these…'

But as soon as she put them on, a powerful energy filled her. She walked with complete grace[34], like an elegant[35] foreign princess.

'Oh, how wonderful tonight will be!' she said to herself as she left.

When she arrived at the palace, the whole party gasped as she walked in, and then clapped. She was even more beautiful than before, and everyone talked about how elegant she looked.

For a moment, the Prince looked sad.

'What's wrong, my Prince?'

'I am amazed by your extraordinary beauty. I have never seen a dress or shoes quite like that… Come, let us dance!'

Cinderella danced with the Prince, and for the first time in many years she felt happy. She felt no worry, no sadness or pain, and when she saw her sisters she did not even feel angry at them, although they certainly felt angry at her.

She enjoyed herself so much that she hardly noticed the time pass. She stared into the Prince's eyes the whole evening, as they had a silent conversation with their bodies.

But then the clock began to strike[36] and Cinderella woke up from her dream. She looked up. It was twelve!

'I'm so sorry, my Prince, but I must leave.'

She moved out of his arms and ran through the hall. The clock struck behind her: two, three, four.

'Wait!' cried the Prince, taking her hand. 'You cannot leave. I must know—'

'You cannot!'

Five, six, seven.

Cinderella pulled herself free and ran outside.

Eight, nine.

But the Prince had predicted that she might attempt a quick escape, so he covered the stairs with glue, and as she ran down them her shoes got stuck[37].

If you stand on glue, your feet will get stuck.

Ten, eleven.

Wanting to get away before the spell was broken[38], she pulled her feet out of the shoes, leaving them stuck to the steps, and ran into the night.

Twelve.

As she ran, her beautiful dress began to disappear, turning back into the ugly rags she had worn before. Her hair turned ragged and dirty, and her worn old working shoes returned to her feet.

Her carriage was gone, and thinking that the Prince would run after her, she ran all the way home.

She burst through[39] the door, threw herself on the floor and started crying. Oh, what a wonderful evening it had been, and how quickly it had gone! Now she had to return to her sad, painful life, and she never even kissed the Prince.

Cinderella cried for several hours, and then dried her face. She couldn't let her awful sisters and stepmother see her tears, so she covered her face with dust to hide the redness in her cheeks.

The rest of the family arrived with plenty of noise, Freta and Greta laughing cheerfully at some joke one of them had made.

'Shh!' said their stepmother. 'You'll wake up the neighbours.'

'Oh, but Mother, it was such a wonderful night! And I *do* believe that man wants to marry me.'

'That man does not have much money. You were supposed to make the Prince fall in love with you[40].'

'But that's not fair! That awful foreign princess stole him away the whole night. What were we supposed to do?'

'You were supposed to do better. Now off to bed.'

Luckily, Freta and Greta did not come in to talk to Cinderella, but her stepmother did.

She stood there in the door with a serious expression[41] on her face. In the moonlight[42] she looked like a dead person who had come out of the grave[43].

'It was a lovely evening, wasn't it?'

'I wouldn't know, Mother, as I was working.'

Her stepmother smiled briefly. 'And you worked very well. I thought that was two nights' work.'

'I did not stop once.'

'How lucky we are to have you, Bridget.'

Cinderella was surprised to hear her name, and her stepmother smiled.

'Remember, my dear, you will always live here. There are no happy endings or handsome princes for you, understand?'

'Yes, Mother.'

'Good. Now get some sleep. From tomorrow, you will be helping Freta and Greta prepare for their weddings, as a man will certainly ask them to marry him.'

Cinderella lay down on the floor and waited for her stepmother to leave. She felt sick. That was what the rest of her life would be: doing everything her horrible step-sisters wanted. Even if they got married, they would bring her with them, making her do all their work.

'Oh, Mother,' whispered[44] Cinderella. 'If only you were here.'

The next morning, the whole family was woken up by a trumpet playing in the street.

'All listen! There is an announcement from the King!' cried a male voice. Cinderella ran to the window. It was one of the King's men, standing on a carriage and reading from a piece of paper. 'The King is searching for the future bride of his son, the Prince. The woman who can wear these shoes and walk gracefully[45] will be the Prince's bride. She must walk "as if on air".'

The man held up a pair of shoes—Cinderella's shoes from the night before! The spell[46] had not taken them. Cinderella's heart beat fast. If she could try them on...

'Me first!' shouted Greta, running down the stairs.

'No, me!' cried Freta.

They started fighting[47], and ended up falling into a pile on the floor.

'Girls!' shouted their mother. 'Get up at once! If you are going to be the Prince's bride then you must act like a princess.'

Cinderella watched as they walked out to try on the shoes. But the King's servant simply held the shoes up to their feet and said, 'Sorry, ma'am, but these feet will never fit into the shoes.'

'Well, aren't you at least going to try?'

'We can't damage them before anyone else gets to try them.' He smiled. 'How about this: if your daughters' feet get smaller in the next few hours, they can try them on.'

Furious[48], the stepmother walked her daughters back inside and said, 'Freta, come with me into the kitchen.'

She took her into the room and shut the door behind her. Confused, Greta and Cinderella looked at each other, but the girl just said, 'What are you looking at, ugly?'

While the stepmother talked to Freta, Greta went to pick out a dress 'for her wedding'.

'I suppose there is no magnificent dress waiting in the tree for me today...' said Cinderella sadly.

With nothing else to do, she went and pressed her ear

to the kitchen door to hear what her stepmother and stepsister were talking about.

'Mother, no!' came Freta's voice.

'Stop crying, child! It will only hurt for a bit, but you will have a life of happiness afterwards. You can pay for new feet when you're Queen.'

'Mother, I'm scared!'

Freta started crying, and then came some sounds of fighting between them, before the girl screamed so loudly it hurt Cinderella's ears.

'Be quiet!' shouted the stepmother.

Cinderella's eyes went wide. She couldn't be...?

After the horrible operation was over, Cinderella ran and hid in the corner. A few moments later, the door burst open[49], Cinderella's stepmother carrying Freta in her arms.

The girl was trying not to cry. Cinderella looked down at her feet. They had bandages wrapped around them, and blood was coming out.

The stepmother carried Freta outside to the King's servant, pushing past the other townspeople.

'My daughter's feet were a little swollen[50] due to the cold weather. The shoes will fit perfectly now.'

Cinderella watched in horror[51] through the window. The stepmother managed to hide the girl's feet until the shoes were on, and then she pushed the girl forward.

'Walk, dear,' she whispered.

But Freta just fell forward like a baby duck, landing in the man's arms.

'This is not the girl,' he said, pushing her back. 'The Prince said she should walk as if on air, not on mud[52].'

Freta burst into tears, pulled off the shoes and ran upstairs. For the first time in her life, Cinderella felt sorry for her.

'Who's next?' called the man.

The stepmother went inside and called Greta in to the kitchen, but after seeing what had happened to her sister, the girl didn't want to go.

'It'll just hurt for a second, dear. Think of how rich we'll be afterwards!'

Cinderella covered her ears, but she still heard the awful screams. Then, when it was over, she went and watched through the window as Greta went to try on the magic shoes.

Greta tried to walk gracefully[53], but it was clear how much pain she was in, and she only managed a few steps before stopping.

'Better,' said the man, 'but not graceful. She is not who the Prince is looking for.'

Greta bit her lip, made herself smile, and handed back the shoes.

'What's all this noise about?' said Cinderella's father, coming down the stairs. 'I heard you screaming,' he said, looking at Greta.

'The Prince is looking for his bride, the mysterious[54] princess,' she said. 'The person who can walk in her shoes can marry him. But, but, but me and Freta couldn't do it!'

She started crying and fell into her father's arms.

'There, there[55], dear,' he said. 'Oh, Cinderella! Why don't you try?'

'Absolutely not!' cried her stepmother. 'She's a dirty servant girl and nothing more.'

'Excuse me?' said her father. 'I told you to stop talking about her like that!'

'Is there another daughter at this house?' said the King's man, hearing the conversation.

'No!' cried the stepmother.

'Yes!' cried the father at the same time. 'She's right here.'

He left Greta and took Cinderella by her arm.

'Don't be afraid, dear.'

'No, that's not fair!' cried Greta.

'Everyone will have a chance,' said the King's man. 'Those were the Prince's words. Now, my dear, here are the shoes.'

The man handed Cinderella the shoes. Cinderella slipped them on.

They fit as perfectly as the night before, and immediately she felt the same magic flowing through her. She

A girl curtseying (pronunciation KURT-see)

raised her head and smiled, walking forward with the grace of a beautiful bird and curtseying to the King's man.

'It's her! I didn't recognise you in the dirt and dust, and wearing such rags, but you are one and the same[56]!'

'I may not be a foreign princess, but hopefully I am enough for the Prince.'

'More than enough!' cried the Prince, and jumped out of the carriage.

He had been hiding there the whole time watching!

'You are a very beautiful girl, and you have had to live with such an ugly family.' He knelt down[57] before her, taking her hand in his. 'I will not ask your father for permission to marry you, because I want it so much that nothing on Earth could stop me. Bridget, will you be mine?'

'Yes!' said the girl, and he pulled her into a kiss.

Despite her dirty appearance, despite the people watching, despite the crying of her sisters and step-mother, it was the most magical[58] moment of her life. Everything else went away, and all there was was her and the Prince.

They had their wedding a few weeks later. Her family had treated her like dirt, but she still invited them all. Her sisters came on crutches, unable to walk properly due to their cut-up feet. Her stepmother refused to come.

Before the ceremony, her father spoke to her privately.

'I'm so sorry, Bridget. I was a terrible father. I pretended[59] not to see, or I wanted not to see, everything that was going on. I

When you hurt your legs, you can use crutches to help you walk.

didn't pay attention to you and focussed on my work, and I let that awful woman hurt you. When I see what she did to her own daughters…'

'What will you do, Father?'

'I am leaving her, and taking Freta and Greta with me.'

Cinderella's heart hurt. For so many years she felt like she had lost her father, but now he was here again. She couldn't lose him again.

'Come live with us, in the castle.'

'I don't think the Prince will want us here after he saw how awful we were. No, we will go and live a simple life, and I will teach those girls to be good and kind. You deserve your happiness, my dear.'

'But you'll come and visit, won't you?'

'Of course. I love you, Bridget. I'm just sorry I didn't show it properly.'

So Cinderella went and got married. But she was not Cinderella anymore, but Bridget, because she no longer had to clean up the ashes and sleep on the floor. She was going to be queen, and she would never have to do such awful chores[60] again, or live with her horrible stepmother and stepsisters.

As the bride and groom kissed, a pair of birds flew happily around them, and far away, in the garden of a certain house, a hazel tree blew in the breeze.

AUTHOR'S NOTE

Thank you so much for reading *Easy Stories in English for Pre-Intermediate Learners*! I hope you enjoyed the book and found it helpful.

If you did enjoy the book, please think about writing a review[1]. Reviews will help other people find the books, and the more people read the books, the more I will be able to write!

If you want language learning advice, you can join my email newsletter. Every two weeks I will send you an email telling you the best ways to study English. If you join now, you can get my free PDF 'My Top 10 Language Learning Advice'.

Go to EasyStoriesInEnglish.com/Email to join! Or you can scan the QR code below:

You can find over a hundred stories, including audio and transcripts, at EasyStoriesInEnglish.com. Scan the QR code below to go there:

Or you can find the podcast on Spotify or Apple Podcasts!

If you *really* enjoyed the book and have something to say, you can email me at Ariel@ EasyStoriesInEnglish.com. I love hearing from my readers and listeners, so don't be shy!

Now that you've read the pre-intermediate level of this book, why not try the intermediate level? Take your English to the next level today!

VOCABULARY EXPLANATIONS AND REFERENCES

WHY YOU MUST READ

1. **Your native language** = the language that you grew up speaking
2. 100 People, *100 People: A World Portrait* <https://www.100people. org/statistics-100-people/> [accessed 4 January 2021].
3. Stephen Krashen, *The Power of Reading - Stephen Krashen* (5 April 2012) <https://www.youtube.com/watch?v=DSW7gmvDLag> [accessed 4 January 2021].
4. **Juvenile delinquent reform centres** are places (centres) to help young people (juveniles) change themselves and get better. These are young people who have done crimes (delinquents). So basically, they are schools to help children who have had serious problems.
5. **Native speakers** = people who have spoken a language all their lives, for example English people are native speakers of English
6. **A study** = an experiment
7. **The Fiji islands** (pronunciation **FEE-jee EYE-lands**) = a country made of islands east of Australia
8. **Sustained silent reading** = reading in silence for a long time
9. Warwick B. Elley, 'The Potential of Book Floods for Raising Literacy Levels', *International Review Of Education*, 46, (2000), 233-255.
10. **To absorb something** = to take something in without thinking, to naturally learn something
11. **A podcast** = a show that you can listen to on your phone, like a radio programme
12. **Fairy tales** = famous stories like Cinderella and Hansel and Gretel, which people usually tell to children
13. Stephen Krashen, 'Aesthetic Reading: Efficient Enough', *Journal Of English Language Teaching*, 62.2, (2020), 3-4.
14. **Technical** (pronunciation **TEK-ni-kul**) = about a specific topic that is complicated, for example computers or science
15. **A study** = an experiment

16. Jeff McQuillan, 'Where Do We Get Our Academic Vocabulary? Comparing the Efficiency of Direct Instruction and Free Voluntary Reading', *The Reading Matrix*, 19.1, (2019), 129-138.

17. **Academic word lists** = lists of words that people need for university.

18. Heather Rolls, Michael P.H. Rogers, 'Science-specific technical vocabulary in science fiction-fantasy texts: A case for 'language through literature'', *English for Specific Purposes*, 48, (2017), 44-56.

19. **To test an idea** = to see if an idea works, to try an idea

20. **A transcript** = when you have a podcast or a radio show and you write down all the words as a text

21. **A podcast** = a show that you can listen to on your phone, like a radio programme

22. **Latin American** = people from Latin America, countries like Peru, Argentina, Mexico and so on

23. **To absorb something** = to take something in without thinking, to naturally learn something

24. Stephen Krashen, 'Self-Selected Fiction: The Path to Academic Success?', *CATESOL Newsletter*, (2020), 1-2.

25. **Second language acquisition** = learning a second language, learning a language that isn't your first language (native language)

26. **Your native language** = the language that you grew up speaking

27. Quote adapted from:

    Stephen Krashen, 'The Case for Narrow Reading', *Language Magazine*, 3.5, (2004), 17-19.

28. **Context** = the words around it, the general meaning around something

29. Marcella Hu, Paul Nation, 'Unknown Vocabulary Density and Reading Comprehension', *Reading In A Foreign Language*, 13.1, (2000), 403-430.

30. **Nonsense words** = words that are not real, words that someone created

31. Here is the text with no nonsense words:

    Jerry jumped out of bed and opened the curtains. He sang to himself as he made breakfast. He poured coffee and put butter on his toast. His phone rang, and he picked it up. He was so shocked by who was calling that he dropped his food on the floor.

32. The idea for this came from:

    Marcos Benevides, *Extensive Reading: How easy is easy?* (2015)

<https://www.slideshare.net/MarcosBenevides/how-easy-is-easy> [accessed 4 January 2021].

33. **A strategy** = a plan of how to do something
34. **To reread** (pronunciation **REE-reed**) = to read something again
35. **I just spent ages** = I just spent a lot of time
36. **To use up time** = to take away time, to waste time
37. **Audio** (pronunciation **AWW-dee-oh**) = sound
38. **An episode** = a part of a programme. Usually there is a new episode every week.

THE NORTH WIND AND THE SUN

1. **To bathe** (pronunciation **BAYTH**) = have a bath, swim
2. When people work well together, they are in **harmony**. They do not fight, and they get on well with each other.
3. **Strength** = being strong
4. **BAM** is a sound you make when you hit something very hard.
5. **Kindness** = being kind
6. **Weakling** (pronunciation **WEEK-ling**) = a weak person
7. If you stop someone from getting air into their body, you **suffocate** them. You can suffocate someone by putting your hands around their neck, but this is not very nice!
8. **Ugh** (pronunciation **UKH**) is a sound you make when you think something is disgusting.
9. A **bitter cold** = a strong cold, an icy cold
10. **An icy cold came over the earth** = Suddenly, an icy cold covered the earth.
11. **Bathed the world in light** = Quickly covered the world with light
12. When it is very hot, or you do a lot of exercise, you **sweat** (pronunciation **SWETT**, past tense **sweat** or **sweated**). Water comes out of your body, and you start to smell bad.
13. **Strength** = being strong
14. **Kindness** = being kind

STRANGE FRIENDS

1. **Chase** = to run after someone, to run quickly so that you can catch someone
2. **Fat** is something we all have in our body. It is under the skin. If you eat a lot of food, you will have lots of fat, but if you eat less food, you will have less fat. We take fat out of animals to use for various things. For example, people often use pig fat when cooking.
3. An **altar** (pronunciation **AWL-tuh**) is a special table that you find in churches. It is at the front of the church.
4. When you are **thankful**, you are very happy that you have something and you say 'thank you' a lot.
5. **To give birth to a child** = to have a child, to finish being pregnant
6. In Christianity, when a child is born, there is an event called a **christening** (pronunciation **KRIH-suh-ning**). You put water on the baby's head, and you give the baby a name. Two friends of the parents become the godmother and godfather. They say, 'I will help look after the child,' and they often give them presents and so on.
7. In Christianity, when a child is born, the parents choose a **godmother** and a **godfather**. They say, 'I will help look after the child,' and they often give them presents and so on. The godmother and godfather are chosen at an event called a christening.
8. When you put your tongue on something, you **lick** it. For example, you lick ice creams to eat them. You lick an envelope to close it. When you lick your lips, it is because you are hungry and you are thinking about food.
9. A **godchild** = the child who a godmother and godfather look after
10. **Assistance** = help
11. **To give birth to a child** = to have a child, to finish being pregnant
12. **To spare** = to give something that you don't have a lot of
13. Someone who is **greedy** wants to have lots of food, or lots of money. Often, children are greedy, and always want to eat more food and sweets. Maybe they steal food from other children because they are so greedy. Usually, when adults are greedy, it means that they want more and more money.
14. '**Good things come in threes**' is a phrase. We say it when we have three good things together.
15. A **paw** is a hand, but an animal's hand. Animals don't have fingers like us, so they have paws. Cat paws are really cute.

16. **To ponder** = to think very carefully about something
17. **To be put off** = to be made less confident, to be less excited to do something
18. When you put your tongue on something, you **lick** it. For example, you lick ice creams to eat them. You lick an envelope to close it. When you lick your lips, it is because you are hungry and you are thinking about food.
19. When you trust someone, but they do something to hurt you, then they have **betrayed** you. For example, if you tell your friend a secret, and then they tell that secret to your enemy, they have betrayed you. If you are fighting in the army, and your friend shoots you in the back, he is betraying you.
20. **To evoke memories** = to bring back memories, to remind you of old memories

THE VERY HUNGRY DRAGON

1. **Salty** = tasting of salt, has salt in it
2. **Vitamins** are things that you find in food. They are very important for our health. For example, we get vitamin C from oranges. Vitamin C is important when you are ill, so when you are ill, people often say, 'Drink lots of orange juice.' Another important vitamin is vitamin D, which we get from the sun.
3. When you **spit** (past tense **spat**), you throw water or food out of your mouth. In the UK, people don't spit outside, but in the past, people used to eat tobacco and spit it out. If you eat some very bad food, you might spit it out.
4. **Rubies** = a type of red jewel
5. **Emeralds** (pronunciation **EM-uh-ruld**) = a type of green jewel
6. **Amethysts** (pronunciation **AM-uh-thist**) = a type of purple jewel
7. **Creep** (past tense **crept**) means to go very slowly and quietly. When you creep, you don't hit your feet down loudly on the ground. Maybe you wake up in the middle of the night and want chocolate, but you don't want to wake up your family, so you creep to the kitchen.
8. **Stomach rumble** = a loud noise your stomach makes when you are hungry
9. Before you eat food, you have to **chew** it. You put it in your mouth and press it with your teeth. Some food is soft and is very easy to

chew, like strawberries. But some food is hard and is hard to chew, like carrots.

10. After you chew food, you pull it down your throat and into your stomach. This is **swallowing**.

11. **Most importantly** = the most important thing was...

12. A **merchant** is a person who sells things. In the past, merchants travelled to different countries and sold things there. Now, we have trucks and aeroplanes to carry things and sell them. A **merchant road** is a road that merchants travel on.

13. **Faraway** (pronunciation **far-uh-WAY**) = a place that is far away, not close

14. Before you eat food, you have to **chew** it. You put it in your mouth and press it with your teeth. Some food is soft and is very easy to chew, like strawberries. But some food is hard and is hard to chew, like carrots.

15. After you chew food, you pull it down your throat and into your stomach. This is **swallowing**.

16. **Eating all of the jewels in one go** = she ate all the jewels at the same time, she ate them very quickly

17. When you eat a lot of food or drink a lot quickly, you might **burp**. You let out lots of air from your stomach very quickly, and it makes a loud noise. It is not polite to burp, so usually only children do it. Some food and drink can make you burp very easily. For example, Coca Cola can make you burp a lot.

18. **Reputation** (pronunciation **reh-pyoo-TAY-shun**) is what people think of you. If you have a good reputation, people think you are good, and if you have a bad reputation, people think you are bad. Reputation is very important for famous people and politicians.

19. When you are very angry at someone because they did a very bad thing, you can say, '**How dare you**?!'

20. **Stomach rumble** = a loud noise your stomach makes when you are hungry

21. **Creep** (past tense **crept**) means to go very slowly and quietly. When you creep, you don't hit your feet down loudly on the ground. Maybe you wake up in the middle of the night and want chocolate, but you don't want to wake up your family, so you creep to the kitchen.

22. When you eat a lot of food or drink a lot quickly, you might **burp**. You let out lots of air from your stomach very quickly, and it makes a loud noise. It is not polite to burp, so usually only children do it.

Some food and drink can make you burp very easily. For example, Coca Cola can make you burp a lot.

23. **Salty** = tasting of salt, has salt in it

DOGGO AND KITTY DO THEIR LAUNDRY

1. When you drop things a lot, or break things a lot, you are **clumsy**. Clumsy people are usually bad at sports, because they cannot move their body well.
2. **Naturally** = of course
3. **Clothing** = clothes
4. When you don't want someone to hear or see you, you **sneak** (past tense **snuck** or **sneaked**). For example, if you want to steal something from your brother's room, you might wait until he is sleeping and sneak inside. You walk very slowly and quietly, and you try to stay in the dark so that people don't see you. Thieves are usually very good at sneaking.
5. On the ends on your fingers, you have nails. When you hurt someone with your nails, you **scratch** them. Cats often scratch people, and it can hurt a lot!
6. **Laundry** (pronunciation **LAWN-dree**) = when you wash your clothes, the clothes that need washing
7. **Lipstick** = makeup that you put on your lips, usually red
8. Before you eat food, you have to **chew** it. You put it in your mouth and press it with your teeth. Some food is soft and is very easy to chew, like strawberries. But some food is hard and is hard to chew, like carrots.
9. **Shone** (pronunciation **SHON**) = past tense of **shine**
10. When it is very hot, or you do a lot of exercise, you **sweat** (pronunciation **SWETT**, past tense **sweat** or **sweated**). Water comes out of your body, and you start to smell bad.
11. When you **spit** (past tense **spat**), you throw water or food out of your mouth. In the UK, people don't spit outside, but in the past, people used to eat tobacco and spit it out. If you eat some very bad food, you might spit it out.
12. When a child is very bad, they are **naughty** (pronunciation **NAW-tee**). For example, naughty children hit other children, steal things and don't do their homework. They are not nice.
13. **Mature** (pronunciation **muh-CHAW**) = behaves like an adult

14. When you move your hand backwards and forwards on something, you **rub** it. For example, when you make a mistake when writing, you use a rubber, or an eraser, to rub out the mistake. When you shower, you rub soap on your body.
15. **To leap** (pronunciation **LEEP**) = to jump very high
16. **Wet the soap** = made the soap wet
17. **To dip** = to quickly put something in water so that it is wet
18. **To leap** (pronunciation **LEEP**) = to jump very high
19. **Dripping wet** = very wet, so wet that water is falling off
20. When you hold something very tight in your hands, you **squeeze** it. For example, when you make some drinks, you might squeeze a lemon into the drink. When you wash your hair, you squeeze the hair to get the water out. If you squeeze your arm very hard, it will go red.
21. **To swing** (past tense **swung**) = to move backwards and forwards, like a pendulum
22. **In no time flat** = in no time, very quickly
23. **Raincloud** = a cloud that carries rain
24. **The actual laundry** = the real laundry, the proper laundry
25. **One step closer** = a bit closer, nearer
26. **Satisfaction** = being satisfied

DOGGO AND KITTY TEAR THEIR TROUSERS

1. **Laundry** (pronunciation **LAWN-dree**) = when you wash your clothes, the clothes that need washing
2. **Their finest clothes** = their best clothes, their nicest clothes
3. **Parasol** (pronunciation **PAH-ruh-sol**) = an umbrella for the sun
4. **Stuck inside** = you're inside and you can't go outside
5. **To adjust** (pronunciation **uh-JUST**) = to move something so that it looks better
6. **Hide-and-seek** is a game that children play. One child closes their eyes and counts: one, two, three, four… The other children run and **hide** somewhere (past tense **hid**, past participle **hidden**). They go somewhere where you can't see them. Then the first child has to find them.
7. **Bush** = a small tree, a short green plant

8. When you **stick out** (past tense **stuck out**), you appear behind something that is shorter than you. For example, if you are very tall and stand behind a wall, your head might stick out.
9. **Paws** = animal hands
10. **To adjust** (pronunciation **uh-JUST**) = to move something so that it looks better
11. **To go for a stroll** = to go for a walk, to take a walk
12. **To giggle** = to laugh nervously, to laugh like a girl
13. **Torn** = past participle of **to tear**
14. **Hide-and-seek** is a game that children play. One child closes their eyes and counts: one, two, three, four... The other children run and **hide** somewhere (past tense **hid**, past participle **hidden**). They go somewhere where you can't see them. Then the first child has to find them.
15. **To untie a knot** (pronunciation **NOT**) = to break a knot, to open a knot, to undo a knot
16. **To peck** = when a bird hits something with its mouth
17. **Violence** = shouting, hurting people, hitting people, breaking things
18. **A seamstress** (pronunciation **SEEM-struss**) = a woman who makes and repairs clothes
19. **To stand guard** = to stand by something and protect it, to wait for someone to come out
20. **Paws** = animal hands
21. **Violence** = shouting, hurting people, hitting people, breaking things
22. **To giggle** = to laugh nervously, to laugh like a girl
23. **It got the job done** = it worked, it was successful
24. **Throughout the night** (pronunciation **throo-AUT**) = through the whole night, all night

DOGGO AND KITTY BAKE A CAKE

1. **To ponder** = to think very carefully about something
2. **To adore** = to love very much
3. **Battered** = old and damaged
4. **A sandpit** = a box with lots of sand in it that children play in
5. **Decoration** = something that you use to decorate
6. **To ponder** = to think very carefully about something

7. **Divine** = very good
8. **To adore** = to love very much
9. When you **pretend**, you do something but you don't *really* do it. For example, if you pretend to eat, you don't actually put the food in your mouth. If you pretend to drink, you don't actually put the drink in your mouth. If you pretend to know something, you say, 'Oh yes, I know that!' but really you don't.
10. **Stomach rumble** = a loud noise your stomach makes when you are hungry
11. A **tail** is a long thing that animals have on their backs. Dogs, cats, foxes and so on all have tails. Humans do not have tails. When dogs are happy, they **wag** their tails, they move their tails quickly.
12. **Five times as good** = 5x as good ('five times five' = 5 x 5)
13. **Unlike** = not like, different to
14. **An egg shell** = the hard outside part of an egg
15. **Balanced flavours** = there is an equal amount of each flavour
16. **Greasy** (pronunciation **GREE-see**) = has a lot of oil in it, has a lot of fat in it, like burgers, chips, bacon and so on
17. A **tail** is a long thing that animals have on their backs. Dogs, cats, foxes and so on all have tails. Humans do not have tails. When dogs are happy, they **wag** their tails, they move their tails quickly.
18. When it is very hot, or you do a lot of exercise, you **sweat** (pronunciation **SWETT**, past tense **sweat** or **sweated**). Water comes out of your body, and you start to smell bad.
19. **Phew** (pronunciation **FYOO**) = a sound you make after you do a lot of work
20. **Massive** = very big
21. **Unlike** = not like, different to
22. **To cool** = to get cold
23. **A windowsill** = the shelf at the bottom of a window
24. When a child is very bad, they are **naughty** (pronunciation **NAW-tee**). For example, naughty children hit other children, steal things and don't do their homework. They are not nice.
25. **Stomach rumble** = a loud noise your stomach makes when you are hungry
26. **To cool** = to get cold
27. **To water** = to make water, to give out water
28. When a child is very bad, they are **naughty** (pronunciation **NAW-tee**). For example, naughty children hit other children, steal things and don't do their homework. They are not nice.

29. **Massive** = very big
30. **Delicate** = easy to hurt, easy to damage
31. You find **mud** outside in the garden. It is brown and has water in it. If you get mud on your clothes, you have to wash them. Pigs love to play in the mud.
32. When you **pretend**, you do something but you don't *really* do it. For example, if you pretend to eat, you don't actually put the food in your mouth. If you pretend to drink, you don't actually put the drink in your mouth. If you pretend to know something, you say, 'Oh yes, I know that!' but really you don't.
33. **Couldn't move an inch** = couldn't move at all
34. When you do something bad and **learn your lesson**, you learn that you should not do that thing again.

SLEEPING BEAUTY

1. **Joy** = happiness
2. **Misery** = being sad, sadness
3. **Pale** = very white
4. **Shone** (pronunciation **SHON**) = past tense of **shine**
5. **Sunlight** = the light from the sun
6. **To dye** = to change the colour of something
7. **A shell** = the outside of an egg, an insect or a nut
8. A **compliment** is when you say something nice about someone else. For example, 'Oh, you look nice today!' or 'You're really good at cooking!'
9. **Gladiator** (pronunciation **GLAH-dee-ay-tuh**) = a man who fights other men in a stadium as a sport
10. **To cheer** = when you are really happy and say 'Yay!' or 'Hooray!'
11. **A throne** = a big chair that the King sits on
12. **A weapon** (pronunciation **WEH-pun**) = a thing you use to hurt someone, like a gun, a knife or a sword
13. **To examine** = to look carefully at something, to look at something for a long time
14. **A figure** (pronunciation **FIH-guh**) = the shape of a person
15. A **wrinkle** is a line in your face. People get wrinkles when they get old. People usually get wrinkles around their mouth, around their eyes and on their forehead.
16. **A raincloud** = a cloud that carries rain

17. **To whisper** = to talk very quietly
18. A **(magic) spell** is a piece of magic. When you are **under a spell**, someone is using magic on you, and they can control you.
19. **Calmly** = in a calm way
20. **To examine** = to look carefully at something, to look at something for a long time
21. **A piece of work** = a creation, something that has been made, an object
22. **Delicate** = easy to break, easy to damage
23. **To ruin something** = to make something bad, to make it so that you can't enjoy something
24. **Spell was broken** = the magic spell was broken, it finished
25. When something very bad happens to you, you **suffer**. You feel very bad. You might suffer because your body hurts a lot, or because people are not nice to you.
26. **Warmth** = warmness, being warm
27. When you **look down on** something, you think that you are better than it. For example, many rich people look down on poor people. They think they are better than poor people.
28. **A healer** = a person who heals, a person who helps with health problems, usually using magic
29. **An entertainer** = a person who entertains, for example a singer or a dancer
30. **To brush your hair** = to put a brush through your hair, to make your hair straight with a brush
31. **Weaker** = less strong, not as good
32. **To hold back tears** = to stop tears from falling
33. **Watery** = made of water
34. **A figure** (pronunciation **FIH-guh**) = the shape of a person
35. **To march** = to walk like a soldier
36. **To whisper** = to talk very quietly
37. **To break something up** (past tense **broke**, past participle **broken**) = to break something into two pieces, to separate something
38. **Unity** (pronunciation **YOO-nih-tee**) = being joined, being together
39. **Joy** = happiness
40. **Bravery** = being brave
41. **Misery** = being sad, sadness
42. **A throne** = a big chair that the King sits on
43. **Dove** = past tense of **to dive** (also **dived**)

44. **Your chest** = the front part of your body between your neck and stomach
45. **A weapon** (pronunciation **WEH-pun**) = a thing you use to hurt someone, like a gun, a knife or a sword
46. **Flies** = small insects
47. When it is very hot, or you do a lot of exercise, you **sweat** (pronunciation **SWETT**, past tense **sweat** or **sweated**). Water comes out of your body, and you start to smell bad.
48. **Bled** = past tense of **to bleed**
49. **Ashes** are what you get when you burn something. When you burn something with fire, it goes black, and then it turns into thin grey things called ashes. When you burn wood, you get ashes. Also, when someone dies, you might have their body burnt, cremated, and then you can keep their ashes.
50. **Darkness** = the dark, being dark
51. **Rose** = past tense of **rise**

ONE-EYED, TWO-EYED, THREE-EYED

1. **Hard-working** = works hard, does a lot of work
2. **An academic** = someone who is very clever, usually a university professor
3. **A fringe** (British; pronunciation **FRINJ**) = hair that goes over your head, hair that goes over your eyes
4. **She is not my type** = she is not the type of woman that I like, she is not the right woman for me
5. **A brat** = a horrible child who behaves badly
6. **A third** = ⅓ (1/3), one over three
7. **Came up to her** = went to her, came near her
8. **To shake your head** (past tense **shook**, past participle **shaken**) = to move your head left and right, to say 'no' with your head
9. **A third** = ⅓ (1/3), one over three
10. **A brat** = a horrible child who behaves badly
11. **Your lap** = the part of your body between your stomach and your knees when you sit down, your legs
12. **To scowl** (pronunciation **SKAUL**) = to make a sound like 'Ugh!' when you are annoyed
13. When you press your hand on something and move it along, you are **stroking** it. For example, if you have a dog who you love, you

will stroke him. You will move your hand up and down his back to show that you like him. You might also stroke your partner's face. If you have a really comfortable sofa, you might even stroke the material. When you're thinking hard, you might stroke your chin.

14. **Smugly** = thinking she is better, feeling better than her

15. **Your lap** = the part of your body between your stomach and your knees when you sit down, your legs

16. If someone is **jealous** (pronunciation **JEH-lus**) of you, they want something that you have but they don't have. For example, maybe you have a Playstation, and your friend wants a Playstation as well. They see you playing it and they feel really jealous. Why can't they have a Playstation, too?

17. **A fringe** (British; pronunciation **FRINJ**) = hair that goes over your head, hair that goes over your eyes

18. **To move aside** = to move to one side, to move apart

19. A **witch** is an evil woman, a very bad woman, who does magic. Witches have black cats as pets, they wear big black hats and fly around. In *Harry Potter*, Hermione is a very successful witch. The musical *Wicked* is about witches.

20. **To nod** = to move your head up and down, to say 'yes' with your head

21. **Laughter** (pronunciation **LAAF-tuh**) = laughing

22. When you do something **reluctantly**, you don't want to do it but you have to do it. For example, most people don't want to get up early in the morning for work. So you reluctantly get out of bed, moving very slowly.

23. When you want to put something underground, you need to **dig** (past tense **dug**). You dig using a wide tool called a shovel, but you can also dig with your hands. When you dig, you make a **hole**, an empty space in the ground. Dogs often dig with their hands and put bones in the hole. In crime films, people often dig holes and put dead bodies in them.

24. A **miracle** (pronunciation **MIH-ruh-kul**) is when something absolutely amazing happens, but there is no explanation for how it happened. In the Bible, Jesus Christ does many miracles. For example, he turns water into wine.

25. **Don't even think about it** = you can't do this, don't try and do this

26. A **witch** is an evil woman, a very bad woman, who does magic. Witches have black cats as pets, they wear big black hats and fly

around. In *Harry Potter*, Hermione is a very successful witch. The musical *Wicked* is about witches.

27. **Bend** (past tense **bent**) is when you take something straight and make it not straight. For example, when you walk you bend your legs. If you bend a small piece of wood, a stick, it might break. Psychics, people with psychic powers, can bend spoons using their minds.

28. **To never lift a finger** = to never do any work, to never help with housework

29. **To test them** = to give them a test, to see if they were good enough

30. **Could not pick a single apple** = could not pick any apples

31. **Frustrated** = annoyed, angry

32. **Roll** is when you move something by turning it around. Balls roll around, because they are round. You can also roll up a piece of paper and hit someone with it. When cars move, their wheels roll along the ground.

33. **To blush** = when your face goes red

34. **Desperate** = trying really hard, trying but failing, wanting something very badly

35. **Overcome with feelings** = she had so many feelings that she didn't know what to do, she had so many feelings she couldn't do anything

36. Fairy tales often end with 'and they **lived happily ever after**'. It means that they were happy for the rest of their lives.

THE BOY WHO KNEW NO FEAR

1. **A good-for-nothing** = a person who can do nothing well

2. When you **shudder**, you shake. You move a bit because you are scared or cold. The hairs on your arms stand up. If you don't want to show that you are scared, you can try and stop yourself from shuddering. But sometimes you are so scared that you cannot stop yourself.

3. **To make a living** = to make enough money to buy food, rent an apartment and so on

4. **Woodwork** (British) = learning to make things from wood

5. **I simply don't understand** = I just can't understand, I don't understand at all

6. **An idiot** = a stupid person

7. **To shut someone up** = to make someone stop talking

8. **Truly** = really
9. **To test someone** = to see if someone can do something, to see how good someone is
10. When you don't want someone to hear or see you, you **sneak** (past tense **snuck** or **sneaked**). For example, if you want to steal something from your brother's room, you might wait until he is sleeping and sneak inside. You walk very slowly and quietly, and you try to stay in the dark so that people don't see you. Thieves are usually very good at sneaking.
11. **Bedsheets** = the sheets you use in your bed
12. **He simply stood there** = He just stood there
13. **That'll teach you** = that will show you, you won't do that again
14. **Constantly** = all the time, again and again
15. **Odd** = strange
16. **Horrified** = very scared or shocked
17. **To cause someone problems** (pronunciation **KORZ**) = to give someone problems, to create problems for someone
18. On the ends on your fingers, you have nails. When you hurt someone with your nails, you **scratch** them. Cats often scratch people, and it can hurt a lot!
19. A **conman** is a man who tries to **con** people. When you con someone, you try to trick them and take their money. For example, someone might talk to you in the street and say, 'I see that you're bald. I have a magic drink here. If you drink it, you will grow hair. You just have to pay me £1000.' But actually, the drink doesn't do anything, and if you buy it, the conman has conned you.
20. **Smugly** = thinking he is better, feeling better than other people
21. When you put your tongue on something, you **lick** it. For example, you lick ice creams to eat them. You lick an envelope to close it. When you **lick your lips**, it is because you are hungry and you are thinking about food.
22. **To sway** = to move left and right, to move from side to side
23. **He had underestimated just how stupid Anders really was** (pronunciation **un-der-EHS-tih-mayt**) = he had thought that Anders was less stupid than he really was, he didn't guess how stupid Anders really was
24. **Fabric** is what you use to make clothes. There are many types of fabric, for example cotton, polyester and nylon. You cut fabric and sew it together to make clothes.
25. **Sewn** (pronunciation **SONE**) = past participle of **to sew**

26. **Foolish** = stupid
27. **Leaping to his feet** (pronunciation **LEE-ping**) = jumping to his feet, jumping and standing up
28. **Payment** = the money someone pays you
29. A **sigh** (pronunciation **SAI**) is a sound you make when you are sad or tired. It is a long, slow breath. When you think of people you loved in the past, you might sigh.
30. When you **frown** (pronunciation **FRAUN**), you push your eyebrows together. When you are confused or angry, you frown. You shouldn't frown too much, though, because then you'll get wrinkles, lines on your forehead.
31. When you put your tongue on something, you **lick** it. For example, you lick ice creams to eat them. You lick an envelope to close it. When you **lick your lips**, it is because you are hungry and you are thinking about food.
32. **Beyond help** = he could not be helped
33. **To get someone's hand in marriage** = to be allowed to marry someone
34. **Your personality** = how you are, for example kind, angry, careful
35. **A haunted castle** (pronunciation **HAWN-tid**) = a castle with ghosts and monsters
36. When you **play a trick on someone**, you trick them in a way that is funny. For example, you say 'Look over there!' and they turn around. But actually, there is nothing over there. While they are looking away, you steal their food. That is playing a trick on them.
37. **Treasure** (pronunciation **TREH-zhuh**) is money, gold, jewellery— expensive things. But when we say 'treasure', we are usually thinking of fantasy and stories. For example, pirates put treasure in wooden boxes called chests and bury them under the ground. Kings sometimes give treasure to heroes. In many video games, you collect treasure.
38. **Odd** = strange
39. A **lathe** (pronunciation **LAYTH**) is a thing that turns something around. So when you make pottery, you use a lathe. Pottery is mugs, pots and so on. You put the clay, the thing you use to make pottery, on the lathe, and it turns it around. Then you use your hands to make the pottery. You can also use lathes to make things out of wood, for example.
40. **Woodwork** (British) = learning to make things from wood

41. **A haunted castle** (pronunciation **HAWN-tid**) = a castle with ghosts and monsters
42. **Lying in ruins** = the building was all ruins, it was old and breaking apart
43. **The darkness** = the dark
44. **The darkness** = the dark
45. Your **eyebrows** are the lines of hair above your eyes. When you are confused or want to ask a question, you can **raise your eyebrows**.
46. On the ends on your fingers, you have nails. When you hurt someone with your nails, you **scratch** them. Cats often scratch people, and it can hurt a lot!
47. **To claw someone's eyes out** = to attack someone's eyes with your claws and take them out
48. **To leap** (past tense **leapt**) = to jump
49. **A beast** (pronunciation **BEEST**) = a horrible animal
50. **At the stroke of midnight** = as soon as midnight came
51. **Crawl** means to move forward by lying down and using your hands and feet. People only crawl when they are trying to stay hidden, for example soldiers who are trying to secretly get into a building. Snakes and insects always crawl, because they cannot stand up.
52. **To flip over** = to turn over
53. **To sit up** = to move from lying down to sitting
54. **The chimney** = a pipe in the roof that smoke comes out of, the pipe above the fire in an old house
55. **Blood was pouring out** = lots of blood was coming out
56. **Evil** (pronunciation **EE-vil**) = very bad, a person who wants to do bad things
57. When you **roll your eyes**, you move your eyes around in a circle. You roll your eyes when someone does something stupid or strange, but you don't want to tell them directly.
58. **Roll** is when you move something by turning it around. So balls roll around, because they are round. You can also roll up a piece of paper and hit someone with it. When cars move, their wheels roll along the ground.
59. **To scare someone** = to make someone scared, to frighten someone
60. **At the stroke of midnight** = as soon as midnight came
61. **Sadly** = in a sad way
62. **A coffin** = a box you go in when you die
63. **He was convinced** = he was completely sure
64. **Foolish** = stupid

65. When you **roll your eyes**, you move your eyes around in a circle. You roll your eyes when someone does something stupid or strange, but you don't want to tell them directly.

66. **A round of bowling** = a game of bowling

67. When you **strangle** someone, you put your hands around their neck and press down so that they stop getting air, so that they suffocate. If you strangle someone for a long time, they will die.

68. **A passage** = a part of a building you walk through to get to another room

69. **To dangle** = to hang down and move left and right

70. **To swing** (past tense **swung**) = to move backwards and forwards, like a pendulum

71. **Trapping his beard inside** = putting his beard inside so that it couldn't move, so that it was trapped

72. **To beat** = to hit again and again

73. **To threaten to do something** (pronunciation **THREH-tun**) = to say that you are going to do something very bad, for example, 'If you don't give me your wallet, I'll beat you!'

74. **Released the old man** = stopped holding the old man

75. **A chest** = a strong box made of wood used to store things

76. **Surely now you have learnt** = You must have learnt by now, I'm sure you have learnt by now

77. **A bearded man** = a man who has a beard

78. **To gasp** = to take a big breath because you are very surprised

79. **Hooray** = a word you say when you are very happy for someone

80. When you **play a trick on someone**, you trick them in a way that is funny. For example, you say 'Look over there!' and they turn around. But actually, there is nothing over there. While they are looking away, you steal their food. That is playing a trick on them.

81. A **sigh** (pronunciation **SAI**) is a sound you make when you are sad or tired. It is a long, slow breath. When you think of people you loved in the past, you might sigh.

82. Fairy tales often end with 'and they **lived happily ever after**'. It means that they were happy for the rest of their lives.

CINDERELLA

1. If your mother dies and your father gets married again, his new wife will be your **stepmother**. In fairy tales, stepmothers are usually horrible people.
2. **To treat someone like dirt** = to act like someone is dirt
3. **Ashes** are what you get when you burn something. When you burn something with fire, it goes black, and then it turns into thin grey things called ashes. When you burn wood, you get ashes. Also, when someone dies, you burn their body, cremate it, and then you can keep their ashes.
4. **A grave** = a place in the ground that you put someone when they die
5. If your mother dies and your father gets married again, his new wife will be your stepmother. If your stepmother has her own daughters, they will be your **stepsisters**.
6. **A ball** = a big party with lots of dancing
7. **To gasp** = to take a big breath because you are very surprised
8. If your mother dies and your father gets married again, his new wife will be your stepmother. If your stepmother has her own daughters, they will be your **stepsisters**.
9. If your mother dies and your father gets married again, his new wife will be your **stepmother**. In fairy tales, stepmothers are usually horrible people.
10. When you **embarrass** someone, you make them feel stupid. For example, if you are with your group of friends, and one of your friends is very short, and you say, 'Hey, shortie! Don't you want to be taller?' they might go red because they're embarrassed. In this case, if other people saw Cinderella, her family would be embarrassed, because she looks so bad.
11. **Holding back tears** = trying very hard to hide her tears
12. A **carriage** (pronunciation **KAH-rij**) is a vehicle, a way of getting around, like a car. Usually, carriages are pulled by horses, and someone sits on top of the carriage and tells the horses to move. Before cars existed, carriages were the main way of travelling.
13. **A nut** = a kind of brown food that grows on trees
14. **A gown** (pronunciation **GAUN**) = a dress
15. A **carriage** (pronunciation **KAH-rij**) is a vehicle, a way of getting around, like a car. Usually, carriages are pulled by horses,

and someone sits on top of the carriage and tells the horses to move. Before cars existed, carriages were the main way of travelling.

16. A **servant** is a person who lives in your house and helps you do things. For example, servants do cleaning, cooking and washing. Servants were very common in the past. The British TV show *Downton Abbey* is about servants.

17. **Elegant** (pronunciation **EH-luh-gunt**) = looks expensive, pretty

18. **To whisper** = to talk very quietly, to talk not loudly, when you don't want other people to hear

19. **The clock strikes eleven** = it is eleven o'clock and the clock makes a loud sound (DONG DONG) eleven times

20. **To stare** = to look for a very long time at something

21. **To mess up** = to make untidy

22. **Chores** = boring jobs that you have to do, for example cleaning the kitchen

23. When you want to grow a plant, you first need a **seed**. A seed is a small, brown thing that you put in the ground. You put water on a seed, and the sun shines on it, and slowly it grows into a plant. You can also eat seeds, and they're very good for you. Common types of seeds are sunflower seeds, pumpkin seeds and sesame seeds.

24. **To gasp** = to take a big breath because you are very surprised

25. **Rudeness** = being rude, not being polite

26. **Mysterious** (pronunciation **mis-TEE-ree-us**) = hard to know, hard to understand, like a mystery

27. **To mess up** = to make untidy

28. **They stuck their heads into the room** = they put their heads into the room

29. **Rags** = dirty old clothes

30. **Common** = normal, poor, not a princess or a lady

31. A **servant** is a person who lives in your house and helps you do things. For example, servants do cleaning, cooking and washing. Servants were very common in the past. The British TV show *Downton Abbey* is about servants.

32. When you want to hurt someone, you might **fight** them (pronunciation **FITE**; past tense **fought**). You might fight them with a knife, a gun, or you can just use your hands. You might fight them with words—an argument. Children sometimes throw food at each other —a food fight. A war is like a big fight.

33. **Common** = normal, poor, not a princess or a lady

34. **She walked with complete grace** = she walked smoothly and beautifully

35. **Elegant** (pronunciation **EH-luh-gunt**) = looks expensive, pretty

36. **The clock began to strike** = the clock began to make a loud sound (DONG DONG)

37. When something **gets stuck**, it stops and cannot move anymore. For example, if you are driving and there is a lot of mud, dirt, your car might get stuck, and then you can't drive anymore. Or maybe you are doing really difficult maths homework and you can't solve a problem. You get stuck, and can't move on.

38. **Before the spell was broken** = before the magic ended

39. **To burst through a door** = to go through a door very quickly

40. **You were supposed to make the Prince fall in love with you** = I expected you to make the Prince fall in love with you, I wanted you to make the Prince fall in love with you

41. **Expression** = how your face looks, for example a happy expression, a sad expression

42. **Moonlight** = the light of the moon

43. **A grave** = a place in the ground that you put someone when they die

44. **To whisper** = to talk very quietly, to talk not loudly, when you don't want other people to hear

45. **Gracefully** = moving very easily, walking in a beautiful way

46. **The spell** = the magic

47. When you want to hurt someone, you might **fight** them (pronunciation **FITE**; past tense **fought**). You might fight them with a knife, a gun, or you can just use your hands. You might fight them with words—an argument. Children sometimes throw food at each other —a food fight. A war is like a big fight.

48. **Furious** (pronunciation **FYUR-ee-us**) = very angry

49. **To burst through a door** = to go through a door very quickly

50. **Swollen** (pronunciation **SWO-lun**; present tense **swell**) = when part of your body gets bigger because you are ill

51. **To watch in horror** = to be very scared and watch something horrible happen

52. **Mud** = wet dirt

53. **Gracefully** = moving very easily, walking in a beautiful way

54. **Mysterious** (pronunciation **mis-TEE-ree-us**) = hard to know, hard to understand, like a mystery

55. **There, there** = what you say when someone is sad and you want them to feel better
56. **One and the same** = exactly the same, the same person
57. **To kneel down** (pronunciation **NEEL**; past tense **knelt** or **kneeled**) = to go onto your knees, to bend down
58. **Magical** = magic, having magic
59. When you **pretend**, you do something but you don't *really* do it. For example, if you pretend to eat, you don't actually put the food in your mouth. If you pretend to drink, you don't actually put the drink in your mouth. If you pretend to know something, you say, 'Oh yes, I know that!' but really you don't.
60. **Chores** = boring jobs that you have to do, for example cleaning the kitchen

AUTHOR'S NOTE

1. **A review** is when you write about a book you read, saying what you liked and didn't like, and give it a rating (1-5 stars).

IMAGE ATTRIBUTIONS

THE NORTH WIND AND THE SUN

'Cold?' by Antoine K is licensed under CC BY-SA 2.0.

THE VERY HUNGRY DRAGON

Dragon by Freepik is from Flaticon.com.

'Breads of Moskovskaya Oblast' by Dmitry Makeev is licensed under CC BY-SA 4.0.

'One whole, deli dill pickle' by National Cancer Institute is in the public domain.

Jewel by Freepik is from Flaticon.com.

Eggplant by Good Ware is from Flaticon.com.

'Bullock cart in an Indian village' by Eyeofshahvali is licensed under CC BY-SA 4.0.

DOGGO AND KITTY DO THEIR LAUNDRY

Paw by Freepik is from Flaticon.com; cropped.

Hooks by Freepik is from Flaticon.com.

'The Religious Kibbutz Movement, Settlements in Israel' by The religious kibbutz archive is in the public domain.

'Diet Coke Mentos' by Michael Murphy is licensed under CC BY-SA 3.0.

'View from the Backenswarft on Hallig Hooge' by Michael Gäbler is licensed under CC BY 3.0.

DOGGO AND KITTY TEAR THEIR TROUSERS

'Greyhound with a brindle pattern' by L. Bower is in the public domain.

'Rose Prickles' by JJ Harrison is licensed under CC BY-SA 3.0.

'A needle and red string' by www.photos-public-domain.com is in the public domain.

'Ficelle de Sisal' by Lionel Allorge is licensed under CC BY-SA 3.0.

Worm by Smashicons is from Flaticon.com.

Spiral by Smashicons is from Flaticon.com.

'Dvojitý rybářský uzel 2, Techmania, Plzeň' by Zpevdeste is licensed under CC BY-SA 4.0.

DOGGO AND KITTY BAKE A CAKE

'Springform Pan with the walls loosened from the finished product.' by RibbonsOfIndecision is licensed under CC BY-SA 3.0.

'Fancy raw mixed nuts macro' by Sage Ross is licensed under CC BY-SA 3.0.

SLEEPING BEAUTY

Fairy by Flat Icons is from Flaticon.com.

'Cloak' by David Ring is in the public domain.

ONE-EYED, TWO-EYED, THREE-EYED

'One whole, deli dill pickle' by National Cancer Institute is in the public domain.

'Grüne Oliven' by A,Ocram is licensed under CC BY-SA 3.0.

'Amneville Bison 27082010 4' by Vassil is in the public domain.

'Male impala profile' by Muhammad Mahdi Karim is licensed under the GNU Free Documentation License 1.2.

THE BOY WHO KNEW NO FEAR

'India's Newest Ship Commissioned. 22 June 1943, Woolston, Southampton. the Commissioning of the Sloop

Hmis Godavari. A17517' by Pelman, L (Lt) is in the public domain.

Rope by Freepik is from Flaticon.com.

Axe by Freepik is from Flaticon.com.

Paw by Freepik is from Flaticon.com; cropped.

Bowling by Freepik is from Flaticon.com.

'Equilateral triangle-01' by Matt Grünewald is licensed under CC BY-SA 4.0.

Skull by Freepik is from Flaticon.com.

CINDERELLA

'Hazelnuts' by Fir0002 is licensed under CC BY-SA 3.0.

Bow by Freepik is from Flaticon.com.

'Lens culinaris seeds' by Rainer Zenz is in the public domain.

'MarmiForoTraianoRoma' by MM is in the public domain.

Female head with ponytail by Freepik is from Flaticon.com.

'AdhesivesForHouseUse004' by Babi Hijau is in the public domain.

'Curtsy (PSF)' by Pearson Scott Foreman is in the public domain.

'Axillary Crutches' by Jessica Fisher is licensed under CC BY-SA 4.0.

Made in the USA
Columbia, SC
08 September 2023

22601474R00093